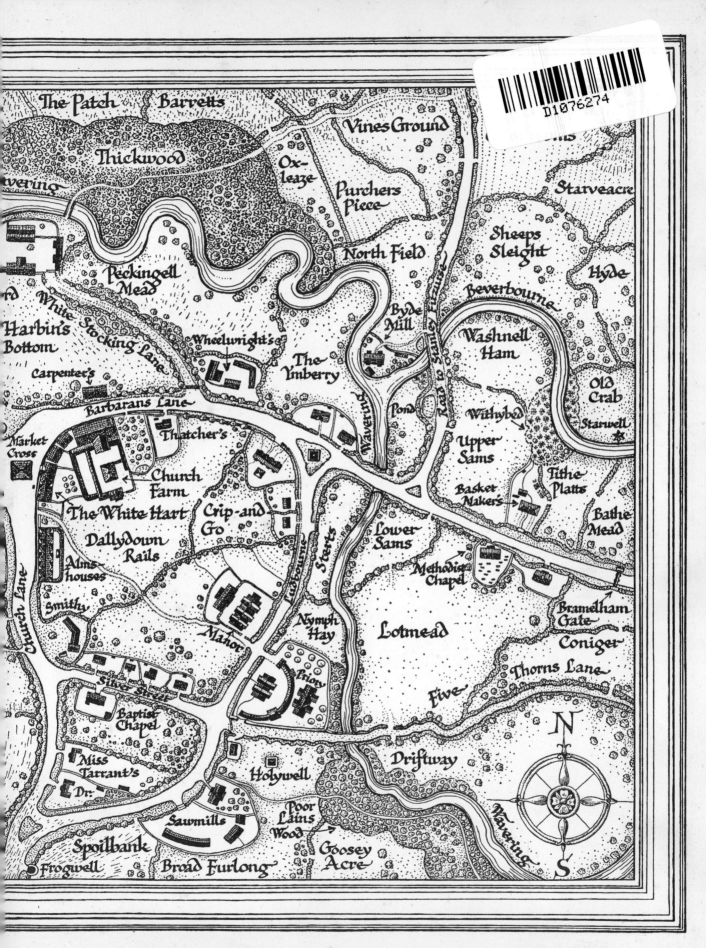

WILTSHIRE VILLAGE

KINGTON BOREL

WILTSHIRE VILLAGE

by

HEATHER TANNER

With Etchings and Pen Drawings
by

ROBIN TANNER

COLLINS
48 Pall Mall London

To Our Parents

FOREWORD

Kington Borel is not to be found on the map, for it is not any one village, but rather an epitome of some of the villages of North-West Wiltshire. The book is to be regarded as fiction rather than as local history; but, like all fiction, it is based on fact. No names that are mentioned fit any actual persons by intention, though they well may by chance, for they are all true to the spirit of the locality, as is the whole matter of the book in every detail. It seemed worth while to try to record some of the characteristics of such a village—the ordinary and typical as well as the more noteworthy—while they yet remain to be recorded. Kington Borel has changed more in the last fifty years than in the five hundred before that; nor have all the changes been for the better. To call back yesterday would be foolish even were it possible; but in order that what was noble in the yesterday that still lingers might not pass unhonoured and unlamented this book has been made.

HEATHER AND ROBIN TANNER

CONTENTS

ETCHINGS

PEN DRAWINGS

PEN DRAWINGS

PEN DRAWINGS

Part One

THE VILLAGE

Its surroundings and character · Its history ·
The barrow · The Saxon charter · Norman
times · The Priory · The church · Flemish
buildings · Farms · Cottages · Wells · The
Almshouses · The Common · The Revel ·
The Nineteenth Century and the changes
of to-day.

KINGTON BOREL lies in the north-west of the county, in one of the shallow combes made by the curves of the Wavering, a tributary of the Avon. The hill at the upper end looks south-east to the Downs, so near that if rain is at hand their folds, the horse cut in the chalk, the clumps of beeches on the horizon, seem but a morning's walk away; so far that in a summer haze they are invisible. All the land between looks almost like the forest it once was, so richly timbered is it, for apart from the woods and copses themselves there is hardly a field that is not hedged by heavy elms. All day the Avon lies hidden, but at dawn the course can be traced by the white mist that hangs above it.

On the other side the hill overlooks the village, which from here appears to lie cosy and compact in a nest of trees, although in reality it has a tendency to straggle in all directions. The Market Cross is its centre, and from it radiate three roads: one, Church Lane, winding in a southerly direction, first uphill, then down to Sutton Pinkney; one running westwards, bordered by a wide strip of common on both sides to the hamlet of Tiddley Winks, and the eastern road, Barbarans Lane, leading to the market town of Bramelham. But to the north the spread of the village is checked by the hilly fields that slope down to the Wavering. The waters of the stream and the woods that fringe it hem in the lands of Kington Borel cosily and protectingly, and beyond is the bleaker parish of Stanley Fitzurse. The

Wavering flows eastwards to the mill, where the tributary Beverbourne meets it, then turns south and meanders through luscious fields towards the Avon.

From a distance, when the sky is cloudy, houses and foliage are the same depth of tone ; but when the sun bursts out and the stone shines brilliantly it seems as though a mirage townlet had suddenly appeared in a green oasis. Beyond the stream the combe rises to a slightly undulating plateau, with more arable land, less pasture, more dry stone walls, less lavish hedges, till in the distance it becomes the wolds of Gloucestershire.

This is, indeed, still Cotswold country. The soil is chiefly cornbrash, with occasional sandy loam or clay, and the limestone is apparent now in outcrops in those few lanes which remain white, now in disused quarries, and everywhere in the houses, that are as natural as animals' homes, fashioned out of the earth on which they stand. And surely man has never found a kinder material to his hand than lies in this belt of oolitic limestone that stretches across the country from here to Yorkshire, throwing up its kindred houses all the way. Here, quite near to the surface, are found the blocks that will make walls, alongside shaly layers that are all but ready-made, ready-graded tiles packed in the soil. This stone is at once soft for hewing and carving, hard for enduring through the centuries. Fresh from the quarry it never looks crudely new because of its broken lines, so alien to the rigid angles of concrete, and because of the ripe warmth of its colour, like the golden crust of a loaf. When it is old and grey it is alive with new growth—emerald moss, orange spots of lichen, stonecrop and rue-leaved saxifrage, pennycress and cobwebbed ivy.

It is not a district far-famed for its beauty; it has seldom been sung by poet or lauded by guide, but it has not gone unrecorded. Along the lane called Waddling Street rode Leland on his way to Malmesbury. A century later John Aubrey, a native of these parts, was testing the waters of Starwell and Holywell for their medicinal properties, and chatting with almswomen who could yet remember when nuns lived in the Priory Farm. His records and, better still, his enthusiasm, were re-discovered by John Britton, whose birthplace was so near Aubrey's own. Britton was at work on his " Beauties of Wiltshire " when William Cobbett was riding, as Leland had done nearly three hundred years earlier, to Malmesbury, venting his indignations and his ecstasies in his journal as he travelled. " The trees are lofty and fine," he wrote, " so that what with the water, the meadows, the cattle and sheep, and, as I hear, the absence of *hard* pinching poverty, this is a very pleasant place." He was strongly tempted to remain and to meddle no more with " cursed politics." " Yes, but then, the flowers, and the birds, and the sweet air ! " But politics won, and he left the county " in as sweet and bright a morning as ever came out of the heavens." It was left to Richard Jefferies, to W. H. Hudson and to Edward Thomas to write, not as court officials, antiquaries, or social reformers, but simply as men who knew and loved " the flowers and the birds and the sweet air."

In such small things the charm of this country lies. Here are no wild mountain peaks, no vast stretches of moorland, no frowning castles, no clear, swift streams with sparkling waterfalls, but gentle hills and smiling valleys, small cosy fields, slow weedy rivulets and humble cottages. It seems that the place has never been uninhabited; one walks in the friendly hollows worn by the footsteps of countless generations.

The Finger-post at the Cross-roads.

Linking the scattered parts of the village are old tracks, some mere field paths, some little lanes, green or paved. Of these the widest is Ludbourne, that skirts the Manor. Where it joins the road is a " tump " or mounded triangle of grass and flowers left undisturbed by the unhurrying traffic of the three converging roads. Many of these little green islands have been removed by the unimaginative fiat of the Ministry of Transport : this one so far remains. On it stands a sign-post which looks like a preaching cross with an oil lamp at the top where the cross should be, and three tiers of stone steps below, where villagers sit and gossip of an evening. It has three arms, ending in crude pointing hands. The eastern one reads : " Bramelham, 4 miles." This road must once have been an old coaching highway, for just beyond Bramelham Gate is a much-weathered milestone, half-hidden by grass, and bearing the inscription, in the fine lettering of a century ago, " 99 miles from Hyde Park Corner." " *From.*" At this stage the weary London travellers must have been wondering if they would ever reach so civilised a place as Bath.

The church, the inn, the almshouses and Church Farm cluster sociably near the Market Cross, and close by is Shepherd's Pond, the largest of the many ponds that dot the village. Some lurk in hollows in the hilly fields—small ponds, these, still and shady, hedged about with brambles, except where cattle have found a muddy entry. There, moorhens build their raft-like nests and boldly lay the generous clutches of eggs in full view, but as safe as though they were hidden with such mud and such thorns to guard them. But Shepherd's Pond is domestic by comparison; it lies open to the sun, and the white tails of dibbling ducks show above its surface like the triangular sails of toy boats. Here the great carthorses stop to drink on their way to the smithy, and heavy-sided cows loiter, knee-deep in the green water, till the herdsman calls to them and they slouch on again, their heads dipping to the rhythm of their gait, their mouths slavering.

A Coaching Milestone.

The earliest trace of man in this neighbourhood is its barrows, both long and round. The nearest, a bowl-shaped one of the early Bronze Age, is in the field called Old Borow at Cold Harbour. When excavated it was found to contain a crouching skeleton and a beaker that had held the dead man's food, beautifully ornamented but in fragments, for at some time in the last century the barrow had been rifled by a farmer in search of stone to repair his cow-byres. Berry Farm, in whose lands it lies, is less than a hundred years old. Yet it has its ghost, or had when Thirza Vines was a girl, for her father once saw it—a milkmaid, carrying her stool. This is most likely her last metamorphosis : the place has been haunted from time immemorial. Else why was it a " cold " deserted place of harbourage on the road that is now a cart track lost in a field ? And why should the Devil turn his Broadstone in the ditch at midnight ? And why did the headless Ralph de Pecquigny, once landlord of the next village, choose this spot of all others in which to walk ? Long before his days the Saxons feared that mysterious mound as the work of Woden, and earlier still the Celtic settlers had woven round it their own dark and primitive superstitions. It was these British people who gave the name of " Cnoc " to Knockdown Hill, and " Lud " to the stream that is now the Wavering. Part of the road that follows its course is still called Ludbourne.

It is the ancient track leading to the barrow that goes by the name of Waddling Street. It was known to be of some antiquity, and was therefore called after the only Roman road the villagers had heard of. There is, in fact, no Roman road nearer than the Fosse Way, though there may have been other lesser ones, for Bath and Cirencester are equally near.

Long ago a Roman coin (so they say) was found in Silver Street, but the small " Roman " horseshoes (five-nailed and wide in the web) that are sometimes dug up and brought to the smithy are more likely Saxon.

And Saxon the county remains for the most part. Its speech has the rich Saxon burr. None but a Wessex man can curl up his tongue to produce this sound ; " foreigners " trying to imitate it can only trill. Saxon are the w's, cropping up where they should not and making havoc of the sounds that follow them. Saxon are the words for fields and tools and for such " whoam " familiarities as consort with " thee bist." And Saxon are the host of short surnames, not lovely to the ear, but robust with a kind of friendly humour—the Chedds and Tucks, the Hudds and Clapps and Bubbs. It was a Saxon thane, Aelfwine, who held the land in the time of the Confessor. Ten hides he owned, and his name is commemorated in Allenford with its hundred-acre farm. Theodwulf—less dignified as the " Tiddle " of later ages—was lord of the neighbouring " wick," now called Tiddley Winks. There are many other names which have survived, like the fossils of lamp shell, trilobite and sea lily in the stone—incongruous reminders that centuries can run concurrent and that man's way of reckoning time is an arbitrary one. Those humble Saxon farmers, Hunlaf and Hearding, Aelfweard and Ealdred, have no need of stone for their memorial, for though we have forgotten them their names are daily on our lips, and the motorist scanning the signpost strangely comprehends a tongue which has not been spoken for close on a thousand years.

" *Endelang Merebrokes* " runs the tenth-century charter defining Aelfwine's land, " *of than broke on Sondermede thar, on of Sondermede adoun to than Lypgate.*" The western end of the village is still called Lypgate, and there actually is a gate here. Twenty years ago it barred the road, and was opened for passing carts and traps by urchins eager to earn a penny. In these days of motor cars it lies open ; but though it is quite useless no one will hear of its being removed. This is all to the good, for some Lypgate or other has stood there for a thousand years, keeping the cattle from straying beyond the common. Bramelham Gate encloses the village at the eastern end. Honeybrook still marks the dividing line between the parishes of Kington Borel and Stanley Fitzurse. " Sunday " Mead is on its northern bank, and farther on it skirts a field whose curious name, " The Ymberry," is, like that of the village of Imber on the distant Downs, a survival of the same old word for a boundary, " gemaere."

" *Of than Lypgate on thar herepath thanne over thane feld, endlang there hegge rewe that Alfric made thar, thanne on than Ellenstubbe,*" the charter continues. There is no trace of Alfric, nor of the hedge he made, in the names hereabouts, but Cookrow, the field path which is a short cut from the pound to the smithy, is linked up with Waddling Street and at the other end with Silver Street and Five Thorns Lane, so it may once have reached the dignity of an " army path " (" herepath ") or main road, and as it happens, the last field it crosses is Ellstubb Patch. " Ellstubb " is a fairly common place-name here, though one would not have thought elderstumps conspicuous landmarks. The elder is a strange shrub, as useless for hedge filling or for firewood as it is useful medicinally, and this may account for some of the superstitions that still persist concerning it—that it was on this tree that Judas hanged himself, that it is a charm against flies, or that witches made their brooms of it. Be that as it may, no man now will cut it down.

There are many other Saxon names: "Great Lynch," a field on the hill to the south of the village, goes back to the days when the slopes were cultivated in terraces, leaving an unploughed strip of land called a "hlinc" to mark the boundary between the fields. "Sterts"—"tail"—is the long narrow field between Ludbourne and the Wavering. "Coniger" is the coneygarth or rabbit-warren. Thickwood, that fringes the Wavering on the Stanley side, appears in Domesday book, but here the scribe was a Norman, and the best he could make of the awkward Saxon speech was Ticoode, a pronunciation not far removed from the local "Dhickood" of the present day.

The Normans, too, left their mark. In the church lies the stone effigy of the crusader baron Richard de Waryn under its crocketed canopy, his legs uncomfortably twisted, his nose battered by nameless vandals, his rusted helm and gauntlets hanging on the wall above him. Close by in the chancel floor the likenesses of his nephew and niece-in-law are engraved in latten. Her hand is in his, and her wimpled head lies on a chequered cushion; he is in armour cap-à-pie. These Gifards and Berengers and Bassetts and St. Quintins stamped their names on the humble Saxon names of the townships they owned much as one would raddle sheep—not from pride of proprietorship, but as a mark of identification; and as sheep they regarded their hinds, not knowing them individually, not speaking their language, but valuing them collectively as a useful means of wealth. The twentieth-century descendants of these hinds have little use for the

Norman names—plain Broughton, Sutton, Wootton and Stanton are good enough for them. But they inherit the one lasting legacy of mediæval times—the feudal spirit; and their bearing towards their squire or lord of the manor is in curious contrast with their yeoman independence, so hardly won through the ages.

By the time Domesday Book was compiled Aelfwine's carucates and virgates had been given by the king to one of his knights. Eventually among other lands they came into the possession of the Waryns, who held them till the fourteenth century, when by marriage they passed to the Borels from whom the village takes its name. One Edward de Waryn, moved by who knows what hope of gaining heaven or of escaping hell, ceded a large portion of his Wiltshire property to the Abbot of Glastonbury. His successor made an additional grant of land for the foundation of a small Benedictine nunnery. The Abbot had his rights of warren, granted him by the king, and the prioress, the lord of the manor and certain privileged tenants had rights of common, the peasants being allowed to common in Herne Wood for part of the year only. Even then there were difficulties, and the Borels were forced to come to an agreement with the Abbot " concerning the impounding of beasts trespassing within the woods of Kington."

Three field names at least are connected with this period of the village history—Peckingell, Pennycroft and Nymph-Hay. Peckingell is mentioned in a thirteenth-century deed, witnessed by Alured Fitzurse, Julian de Waryn, Walter de Cahaignes, " et aliis." " Know that whereas Robert, Lord Abbot of Glaston, has granted to us (Henry Bosket and Alice his wife) for life half an acre which Johan Gengel of Kingtone once held there and by reason of his poverty surrendered, rented at twelve pence or one sheep of the same value and the customary service of mowing Pegingehulle Mead, the same shall revert at our death to the said Abbot." In the days when Pennycroft stood " between the croft of John the Miller and that of Walter de la Yate " it was conveyed with other lands by Hugo de Pecquigny to Robert, a monk of Glastonbury " out of special love to the said Robert." With it went " a Mill and Pond, near the spring called Maydenwell, in the manor of Kingtone, for the supply of the mill pond. Also five perches of land lying under Bidemille Mill in the North field."

Most romantic of all is Nymph-Hay, a seventeenth century corruption of Minchinhay, the " nuns' field," where once might have been seen " two score and ten Nunnes with lay sisters, as widowes, old maydes and young girls, come forth in a morning with their Rocks (distaffs) and Wheeles and Bobbins to spinne, and with their soweing work." The meadow is bounded by a hedge full even to this day of barberry bushes " which " (says Aubrey) " 'tis likely the Nuns used for confections, for there were anciently no apothecaries or surgeons ; the gentlewomen did cure their poor neighbours ; their hands are now too fine." Matins and nones and vespers apart, there was plenty of work to superintend—the taking of corn to the mill or " fish, eggs, butter and such small gear " to the Friday market, or the occasional drawing-up of an inventory—" a boke of Seynts' Lyves yn Englishe . . . a bone of St. Christopher closed in cloth of gold, a noble Relyke . . . a Pylow and two fair Coverlettes." One wonders how Dionysia, the " faire yong woman of Bristowe," Avice, Joan, Cæcilia, Christina, Alys

and their sisters found time to become " guilty of incon-
tinence," and why, in such a golden age, the Prioress ever
found it necessary to erect a gallows.

You may yet see the chapel of the fifteenth century priory
that was built on the site of the earlier one if you look closely

Priory Farm

at the dairy of Priory Farm, with the blocked-up doorway in
its south wall and the curious little window in its gable-end.
If you searched the outlying farm buildings, and others in
the village, you would find many more of the missing stones
filling gaps in walls and ornamenting sundials. For after the
Dissolution the new owner, Francis Everett, finding the

priory a small place and in need of repair, decided to pull it down and use it for the renovating of the manor house close by. Others, too, used it as a quarry, and not one stone would have been left standing had not a certain steward of the manor, one Sir John Pierce, found that part of it at least could be converted into a goodly little farm. He was a man with an eye to the main chance and, arriving on the scene when the village was at the height of its prosperity, made a fortune for himself at his lord's expense, adopted a coat of arms and, to perpetuate his memory, had a large coloured tomb erected by his heir in the church of St. Giles.

It was already an old church. The nave and chancel had been built in the twelfth century. At about the time of the founding of the Priory the darkness within was lightened a little by single lancet windows, the meeting-place of nave and chancel was crowned by a turret with two bells, and a simple south porch was made, thus protecting from the weather the cushion capitals and the crude carvings on the tympanum of the Norman south entrance, which retain the crispness of their outline even now. Late in the fourteenth century both nave and chancel were given an open-timbered roof with collarbeams and windbraces, making the whole church look like the great fifteenth-century tithe barn at Priory Farm. For in this country, where such fine and durable material lay ready to hand, all buildings were necessarily beautiful; barns, byres, churches and cottages were made of the same stone and conceived on the same generous plan, and they are clearly of one family. Indeed, the great tradition of ecclesiastical architecture lingered in the domestic buildings of this part of England later than elsewhere. The barton was planned like a miniature township; the homestead, solid and stately as a manor, was surrounded by its village of out-buildings, with their dovecotes, hipped roofs and trefoiled coping-stones ; the pillared cow-byres were like abbey cloisters. The great barn, lofty as a church, had, like a church, its buttresses and porches without, its nave and transepts and narrow deeply-splayed windows within, its cross-shaped slit high up in the gable at the east end, and finial crosses on its roof.

The strong and lasting influence on this local tradition of building was the work of the Flemish weavers, who came over from the Low Countries and, settling in the neighbourhood, made for themselves stone houses of exquisite proportion. Here they set up a clothiers' cross in the market-place. It has a square base, with a solid square pillar at each corner, and is crowned with a high-pitched tiled roof ending in a carved finial. The wealthy wool-staplers built a fine church, with aisles, transepts, large windows, chapels and a massive tower with crocketed pinnacles in Sutton Pinkney. To the old church they gave a large chancel window.

As the village grew, more farms were built, and more houses, the largest of which is still called Weavers' House. In the seventeenth century it was a cloth mill, but when it ceased to be " full of lumbes to weve clooth yn " it became a farm. It is a large but simple two-storeyed building, lighted by ample stone-mullioned windows. They are all alike, and the beauty of the house lies in the rightness of its relation-ships—the correspondence of breadth with length, of length with height, of storey with storey, of small rectangle of pane with larger rectangle of window, of window with space between windows. The only adornments beyond the sheer requirements of building are the stone parapet which hides the lines of the eaves and the shell porch over the door. On the other hand, with the Flemish Cottages that stand just beyond the pound, the beauty is one of variety—or, rather, of variety in uniformity, for although no two houses are identical in design, they are all of one tradition. Here are two dormer windows next to three high, unmistakably Flemish gables; this cottage has bay windows, roofed with stone tiles; the windows of the neighbouring house have three lights in the lower storey, two in the upper; here is a square doorway, here one with a stone porch and steps, and here the fifteenth-century depressed arch. These buildings are best seen in strong sunlight or when the full moon is high. Then the contrasts of light and shade are brought into play—the sharp angle of a gabled shadow black against the white face of the wall; the dark hollows in the mouldings round the doorways or under the dripstones.

The White Hart was most likely a Flemish building too; it stands quite near, opposite the Market Cross. It is a good house, three-gabled like the Manor, and it does a good trade, for it has been the only public house ever since the thatched cottage at Cold Harbour ceased to be a malthouse with an off-licence. Nearly every household, however, brews its own potent wines in season—dandelion, cowslip, rhubarb, potato, currant, gooseberry, elderberry or parsnip, and nearly every larder has its bungcask and its firkins, their corks attached to the handle with string, lest when with a loud report they fly off they should be hard to find again. There is very little connection in the villager's mind between home-made wine and beer. The one is for family gatherings at Christmas, or for other occasions when hospitality is called for—when, for instance, neighbours lend a hand with the coercion of a recalcitrant pig into the market wagon: the other is an excuse for a social evening after a hard day's work.

Most of the village buildings are of the seventeenth century. The Manor, which represents the most dignified and imposing of the three types of farmhouse to be found here, is still older. It is a rectangular three-storeyed building. The

Kington Borel Manor Farm.

top storey has on both its long sides three gables whose ridges are on a level with that of the main roof; seen from above, the house resembles a church nave with three transepts. Each gable has a mullioned window with two lights; the windows immediately below these in the second storey have three lights, and those on the ground floor have four, so that the three pyramids of windows echo the shapes of the gables. Two groups of fine chimneys are set diagonally on the roof. The Manor is still owned by an Everett; on the death of the old Squire it passed to his granddaughter, the last of the family. The farming of the Manor estates has for centuries been carried on by the tenant of the old Priory.

Allenford Farm and Hill Farm are double houses; each is like two joined back to back, and so it virtually was when the farmer shared it with his sons' families. Hill Farm has a little tiled passage running from roof to roof, linking the two halves of the building.

Priory Farm, being part fifteenth-century nunnery, is not a typical farmhouse, but the grouping of the homestead is characteristic. The barns and outbuildings cluster in a semicircle, of which the farm is the centre; the cow-byres sweep in a crescent on either side of the granary, and behind stands the tithe barn. Church Farm, on the other hand, is serried in a square, like a small, well-planned town with its dark stone gables, bright domes of straw, walled streets of buildings and ricks, shaded here and there by elm or chestnut, and open square surrounded by its pillared colonnade. The homestead is shut off from the farmyard on all sides by walls. That enclosing the kitchen garden is high, and is protected from the weather by a coping of thatch. A door leads into the orchard, which is also poultry-yard; the henhouses stand under the apple-trees, and there is a pond for ducks at the farther end. The big yard nearest the house has on one side the thatched garden wall, on the adjacent sides pigstyes and a byre in which farm carts are kept, and on the fourth what looks like a long barn. This is the stable, and in the loft above are stored, besides hay, apples and potatoes. Rats and mice that would fain make short work of these delicacies are kept down by the fox-terrier, the farmyard cats and their kittens.

Hill Farm.

The second yard, which is divided by a stone wall from the first, contains the corn ricks and the big " stavel " barn. A calving shed and cowbyre have been built on to it, with the barn wall as their back and their pillars flush with the great doors of the threshing-floor, which is raised above ground level on short staddles—hence the name " stavel barn." This lean-to arrangement (which is called a skilling) though it destroys the true shape of the barn, utilises the available space to the full. The cowbyre turns at right angles and runs the whole length of the yard, the whitewash of its massive cylindrical pillars throwing the inner gloom into even sharper contrast. Close to the barn is the granary, a two-storeyed building whose upper floor is approached by a flight of stone steps against the outer wall. The gable-end is of elm boarding, weathered to a silvery grey. Half the ground floor is stable, the other half an open shed for wagons. Under the stone steps is a square recess, big enough to shelter dog-kennel, churn or pail.

Church Farm.

Maslin Farm gets its name from a Thomas Maskelyne who owned it in the reign of Henry the Eighth. It lies outside the parish, at Mount Pleasant, and in those days had a private chapel, used as a place of worship for the cottagers who lived near till the beginning of the century, but now part of the barn. The home pasture is still called Chapel Ground. The house itself is the simplest type of farm—a long rectangular building with a high-pitched hipped roof set in two planes so as to allow of roomier attics with dormer windows ; the attic floors are on a level with the window-sills. As in most farms, the house was formerly divisible into two distinct parts, one for the farmer, the other, with a separate staircase leading into the kitchen, for his unmarried labourers. This segregation, no longer needed as household economy, is typical of the weekday and Sunday sides of the farmer's life. The day's work is done in the big, pleasant, stone-flagged kitchen, smelling of cows and meal, and in the byres and barns, orchards and meadows seen from its windows. Before the front of the house is spread a trim lawn bordered with formal beds that ring the changes on wall-flowers and tulips, begonias and cherry-pie, and geraniums, calceolarias and lobelias. Two rooms overlook this garden. One is the solidly-furnished dining-room, used in the evenings and on Sundays after Mr. and Mrs. Freeth have returned from chapel in their ponytrap. The other room is only opened for callers and for its weekly clean. It is full of ferns and family photographs, and smells damp and airless.

The Freeths have two sons, and a daughter who has charge of the poultry and the dairy. She still churns every week twenty pounds of butter, yellow in summer, white in winter, and makes cheese. Above the dairy is the cheeseroom where the fat round cheeses, covered in home-made fashion with oddments of striped prints and sprigged muslins, sit maturing in rows on long shelves and benches, their strong smell tempered by the cidrous scent of the apples that lie on the floor. The stout rafters of the attic gable rest on short transverse beams which are themselves strengthened by wall timbers shaped like gate-posts, giving the room a kind of primitive hammerbeam roof. Downstairs, besides the usual

The Cheese Room with the old Press, at Maslin Farm.

things found in a dairy—wide pans, butter pats, churn, milk cans, scrubbing brushes, baskets, scales, smocks and saltbox —there are the great wooden troughs and the press itself, a mediæval-looking engine with big circular leaden pans whose double lips look as though in the making the lead itself had begun to boil over and had then congealed into a spout.

Under the cloisters that run in an L along two sides of the dairy the cans and churns are put to dry, for Joe Freeth, the younger son, has a milk round. Since all the other farms sell their milk by the gallon to the condensed milk and the butter factories, he has to call at nearly every house in the village. He starts out at half-past six every morning in his milk float, down the long rough lane and past the big barn with its pigeon-holed gable-end, the thatched byre which flanks the old chapel, and between the aisles of golden corn ricks and dark bean ricks. These are shaped like humming-tops and are ornamented with neat finials fashioned into crowns or birds and reminding one of the poppy-heads on the choir-stalls in the church. Safeguarded from damp and from vermin, the ricks stand high on beds of faggots spread over staddles, and in the little dark underworld beneath these great stone mushrooms cocks and hens scratch and scuffle.

The cottages of Kington Borel are chiefly the plain four-square kind such as children draw, but perfect in scale, with a string-course marking the division of the storeys, drip-stones above the windows, finely-moulded lintels and mullions and graded stone tiles. The tiling of such roofs, that appears to be so simple, is a highly specialised craft known only to local workmen long practised in the tradition, and having, like all crafts, its own vocabulary of technical terms that varies in different districts. Each tile, according to shape or size, has its special name, some denoting measurements of length long since archaic, some obscene, most sounding to the lay ear purely arbitrary. A well-made roof, if kept free from moss, will remain weatherproof for a century. Some cottages have roofs of straw thatch instead of stone tiles—the combination of thatch and stone being an interesting characteristic of the locality. The newly-quarried stone has, like new thatch, a warm golden colour, and older stone, of a ripe brownish-grey, is the colour of thatch when it is weathered.

The Village Well-house.

A Cottage Well.

To-day these houses which have been lived in for close on three centuries would be called inconvenient. The front door usually opens into the living-room, and the stairs lead straight into the main bedroom, which gives into a second, smaller room. All the cooking was formerly done over a large fire, which had a baking oven built into the side of the chimney-piece, for in those days every housewife was her own baker. Nowadays, instead of hearth and bread oven, one generally finds a barred grate, narrow from front to back, and on either side small ovens whose tops make useful hobs. There is, of course, no "indoor sanitation," but the earth closets, though small and dark and inconveniently far from the house, are, like everything else, well built, of stone with stone tiles. The seats are of the companionable double variety, and since vines were found to flourish there, they were often planted to grow up the walls and over the roof, making the place look as cosy and picturesque as a summer-house.

Water is drawn from the garden well, or from a pump or wellhouse shared by four or five cottages. The largest in the village stands in the undivided garden of the houses at the end of Ludbourne. It once supplied a larger community, for its proximity to Bydemill shows it to be the Maydenwell of the deed concerning the Glastonbury monk beloved of Hugo de Pecquigny, though it has lost its name with the need for one. The well-head has a flat parapet, wide enough and low enough to sit on, and over the whole of the square-flagged platform that surrounds it is a pyramidal tiled roof very like that of the market cross, save that the stout stone pillars which support it are cylindrical instead of square. Common property also is the long ash stick, crooked at the end as it grew, with which the bucket is lowered. The cottage well-heads are sometimes square like this one, sometimes horse-shoe shaped and shut at the open end either by a single stone slab which grown-ups can lean over, but which children cannot easily climb, or by a wooden gate. The coping of flat stone is more convenient for resting the bucket when it comes up ; but safer, where there is a young family, is the method of topping the wall with " cockups "—that is, by piling up the stones endwise like plates in a rack. Frogwell, by the roadside on the way to Sutton Pinkney, is of this type. It is circular, except where its gate slices off a segment. All the

Old Maydenwell

41

long way down to the surface of the water the tunnel is green with a rich growth of hartstongue and polypody ferns, liverwort and mosses. With the sunny road in front and the open field behind, the well looks anything but sinister, yet it was from here that the body of Joshua Vizzard was recovered one February afternoon. That night his daughter was born. She was christened Hilda, but every one calls her

Frogwell.

Tiddle—a childish name best suits one who can never grow up. Joshua would most likely have found a pond or a gun even if a well had not been handy. He was a morose man and a heavy drinker; on the night when he disappeared he was on his way back from the White Hart. A traveller cannot fall into Frogwell inadvertently, and in spite of the number of wells and ponds and streams accidents are rare; but the villagers were taking no risks, and what with the rough edges of the coping, the padlock on the gate and the iron grid over the shaft itself, Frogwell is now fairly impregnable.

Starwell is in the parish of Stanley Fitzurse, though it is

Stars in Starwell.

nearer to Kington Borel. The field in which it lies had been nicknamed Starveall on account of the poverty of its soil, but the corruption has some justification, for in the water are found tiny fossilised starfish. The waters of Holywell, near Priory Farm, may have contributed to the efficacy of the simples and salves the nuns made, for they are supposed to be remarkably healing to the eyes. Mothers still send their children with bottles to catch the drops that percolate through the moss and small ferns at the back of the walled cavity in the hillside. So limey is the water that the roots of the moss are petrified into fine brittle coral, and tiny stalactites hang from the roof of the miniature cave ; for children, the magic of the well lies here.

There is another handsome communal well opposite the Flemish buildings. This one has been covered in and the water is pumped up. It has a conical tiled roof, and its wooden posts, each supported near the top by curved beams branching off at either side like a roof tree, make a circle of arches round it. Unlike the square well-house, this one stands in the road itself, and is a favourite place even in wet weather for a good gossip while neighbours wait their turn at the pump. The hill behind the Flemish houses is called Pump Hill. In reality it takes its name not from the hill, but from the " pill " or little creek below it, where Honeybrook flows ; not from the well-house, but from the village pound on the green. At a distance the pound looks like a rather large rectangular well-enclosure, with a gate in one wall. Nobody can say when it was last used (for its rightful pur-

Mrs. Keynes' Cottage and the Pound

pose, that is, for when the schoolchildren come out to play on the green they enjoy chasing Farmer Drewett's cows into it if they are sure Teacher Miles is not looking). The only villagers who still call the place Pound Pill are Joe Garlick and his few contemporaries, and the younger inhabitants ascribe this obstinate whim to illiteracy. So in thirty years' time (for even in this village, renowned for its longevity, Joe is not likely to live to be more than a hundred) a word that has been handed down from father to son since the time of the Britons will have gone from the Kington vocabulary.

44

The dwellings provided for the deserving poor were even more comely than the labourers' cottages. Ever since mediæval times there had been " poore almswomen " maintained by the Church; and in the seventeenth century, thanks to the munificence of one Thomas Westmead,

Thomas Westmead's Almshouses

broadweaver, almshouses were built for such needy and aged persons. They are six cottages joined lengthwise, each with its gable and mullioned windows. Their front windows look out over the churchyard across the road; from their cloisters at the back, that run the whole length of the building, the almswomen can see the Manor and Priory Farm. Every afternoon when the milking is done they take their jugs and go across the field to the dairy to fetch their milk for tea. When the grass is laid up for hay and they go

45

in single file along the narrow footpath, wearing their sunbonnets, they look like a line of white ducks. Polly Fry,
herself an almswoman, made all six bonnets, and could make
them again, for all her seventy-eight years, if they should at
last wear out with constant starching and goffering. She
never measures any one : there is one bonnet, and she can
make no other. She makes it as she was taught by her aunt,
who was a lace-maker at Malmesbury, with " poll-piece " at
the back, double hood to turn back in the front, gathered
" curtain " round the neck, little bow in the nape (this has
no function, but it is imperative that it should be there) and
strings which always remain untied. The main part, which

Polly Fry's Sunbonnet.

46

is gathered into the poll-piece, must have its right quota of tucks and pipings of bonnet-cotton—three rows of piping, a tuck; one row of piping, a tuck; two rows of piping, a tuck; and so on. In her younger days Polly used to be kept busy supplying the Bramelham shops: now there is no demand save from her neighbours.

Thomas Westmead came of good old stock. His grandfather had hoped to style himself " gentleman," but at the Heraldic Visitation was recorded as a disclaimer, while the less deserving Sir John Pierce had been graciously allowed to bear arms. But Thomas could show a long local pedigree, for the West Mead, where had dwelt the first of his name, was the green which reached from this to the neighbouring village and, after the Reformation, was common land to them both, the lord of the manor sharing a generous expanse of land and copse—some three hundred acres in all—with his tenants. The copyholders were allotted each a certain part, and the freeholders paid a small rent for theirs, usually in kind, for it was easier to find a couple of geese yearly than the equivalent eightpence. Here they grazed their cattle, sheep and pigs, kept hens and ducks, and in Herne Wood they gathered their bavins for firewood. The copse was allowed to grow for seven years and then was rented by the " farrendel " (farthing-deal or quarter-acre) for cutting. From this wood, too, might be taken thorns, or hazel twigs for " edders " " for unsuffycyency thereof " in the fields themselves, for the tenants for the time being had to maintain their fields in hedging and ditching and " yate, if any, taking All such frythe and shrowds as there growethe for the necessary Reparacyons of the Shards and Beaten places of the

Grounds, So that the same Shards and Beaten Places doth not extend more than half a lugge in one place." "Shard" has always been the local name for a gap in the hedge. At Butt Rails compulsory military service in the form of archery practice was formerly required of the village youths, and in Lotmead was "great meriment every yeare" when the haycrop or (after the "yeemath" or second crop was reaped) the winter herbage was allotted to the villagers in rotation. Since the eighteenth century these two fields have belonged to the Manor.

For by the time the present vicarage was built the only land left unenclosed was the wide common on either side of the road at the western end of the village, the private estates in the vicinity having swollen as this had shrunk. And not even here were the tenants' horses suffered to graze, for the old autocrat, Squire Everett—the last squire to be given the title—reserved it entirely for his wild hunters, and there they roamed at will, to the terror of passers-by. When at last he died the villagers had almost forgotten it was their land ; but when they did begin to realise their freedom it was with a new jealousy. To-day they present a united front in defence of their territory against either the depredations of individuals or the more insidious encroachments, in the name of road developments, of the County Council. "Our common," however, is treasured rather as a handsome possession than as something to be used, and although children play their games there and ducks swim on the pond, it is only Caleb Drewett of Church Farm who still thinks it worth while to pay twelfth shillings per cow per year to turn out his herd on May the twelve—and even he makes no hay and employs no cowherd. Since, however, he is liable when his cattle cause an accident on the road if they are unattended, he bribes some child who has just left school and has not yet found work, or who for some other reason, such as holidays or measles, happens to be at large. The child finds some cronies and sits by the roadside with them playing " dibs," while the cows wander at their own sweet will. If a gate has been left open and an animal enters a garden in search of more exciting pasture than the common affords, the joint company of cowherds, roused by the shouts of the owner of the garden, join in the hue and cry.

Cows, directly or indirectly, earn the living for half the inhabitants of Kington Borel—the farmers, the labourers, the workers in the distant milk factory. The cows own the common ; theirs are the ponds and theirs the fields. At half-past three, the time of afternoon milking, when Allenford cows are being driven from the Ymberry down White Stocking Lane, Berry Farm cows are plodding up Waddling Street, that is worn into parallel ridges by the daily tread of their hoofs, the Maslin Farm herd are coming from Long Summers and the Church Farm milkers from Ellstubb Patch and Lower Common, it seems as though they were sacred beasts, ponderously re-enacting some old rite of marking out their domain before Lypgate and Bramelham Gate closed it in for the night.

There was one custom, connected with the common, that died hard—the holding of the annual Revel. It had been an ancient privilege, for King Edward the First had granted the Abbot of Glastonbury the right to hold a fair on the vigil of the consecration festival—St. Giles's Day, September the First—the day itself and the following day, and it had been held ever since with but one serious interruption. That was in 1608, when the plague came and carried off eighteen inhabitants, eight of whom were from one family, in three months. Then special constables were appointed in Bramelham, four miles away, to prevent any kin of the stricken folk from entering, and the holding of the Revel was forbidden. In Aubrey's time it was " one of the eminentest feasts in these parts." On the Vigil, a Gilesman was appointed to collect the money required for the ale and the stubble geese, and to see that there was a sufficiency of trenchers—treen dishes, they called them—and spoons and crocks and pewter at the church-house, ready for the Revel. It was now customary to celebrate it on the first Sunday within the octave of the patronal festival. There was a saying that if that day were fine there would be good weather for the next fourteen days, and indeed " St. Martin's Summer " often set in at about that time. On the day of the feast there were archery contests on the green, and dancing and games such as bowls, quoits and " stoball," a kind of golf played with a long ash stick and a hard leather ball stuffed with goose quills. The profits of the merrymaking (after Sir John Pierce had taken ten shillings' or so toll for his master) were used to buy a new bell for the tintinnabula, or to pay for the washing of surplices, or " for the nursynge of a poure childe which is nursed at the charges of the parish " or charity to some " maymed souldier that came from the spittal house." For although there were poor boxes at the church and at the inn, and although collections were sometimes made " for the poore sufforors in Ireland " or some other remote cause, there was no poor rate, and the Church, which was then the centre of the social life of the parish, relied mainly on the Revel money

and on that obtained from the selling of the Whitsun ale
brewed by the churchwardens for the maintenance of its
parish paupers.

The oldest villagers can remember when the Revel was
celebrated outside the White Hart. Worthy Vines, who was
Gilesman on several occasions, kept the inn then, and had
set up there the first village bakery, still maintained by his
grandson, George Knapp. Perhaps that was partly why
lardy cake had replaced the stubble goose. The lardy, hot
and greasy from the oven, is still the Wiltshireman's favourite
Saturday tea. It is made of dough left over from the bread-
making, rolled out and spread liberally with lard, sugar, well
" plimmed " currants or sultanas and spice—sometimes with
candied peel too—and folded over, spread, and rolled out
again and again like flaky pastry. Then it is scored across the
top and baked in squarish, well-greased tins, so that when it
comes out it looks like a flat mediæval loaf with rounded
corners. The perfect lardy is flaked on the top, fatty and
rather treacly on the bottom; and between, the shaly layers
of rich dough should be neither too close nor too light in
texture. It is said that nobody, not even George Knapp, who
uses the same recipe, can make lardies as Worthy Vines
made them.

There were other changes in the celebration of the Revel.
It was no longer held on a Sunday but on a Saturday, and
with the change of day was losing its religious character.
The chief meal of the day was eaten at home, after work.
The pudding was always blackberry tart and at the Revel
every one wore his " bunch of four "—a cluster of four hazel
nuts, whose symbolic cross shape was a reminder, or should
have been, of the origin of the festival. Neither blackberries

nor nuts were really ripe, but the children could always find
enough for the occasion, especially if they hunted in the high
sheltered hedges of Pennycroft.

But though children still ransack Pennycroft for early
blackberries, there is no longer a Revel. The last was held
in 1890. Perhaps it was gradually ousted by the rival attrac-
tions of Bramelham Long Fair which, with its merry-go-
rounds, swingboats, houp-las and coco-nut shies, made the
village festival seem a falling-off indeed. Perhaps it was
decided to combine it with Harvest Home, which was kept
up for three nights running with good rustic cheer—mutton
and turnips, beer and beef, potatoes and pudding, till the end
of the last century.

On the whole things moved slowly here. Great changes
such as the Industrial Revolution left little mark, for by then
the wool trade—that in Leland's time had been so flourishing
that he found " every corner of the vaste houses of office
that belongid to thabbay " of Malmesbury " full of lumbes
to weve clooth yn "—had moved North. The only machinery
in the village was the sawmills—unless one counts the looms
of the seventeenth-century mill. The sawmills were started
early in the nineteenth century, and the owner, Daniel
Jeffries, who came from Highworth, settled in one of the two
fine houses that had been built some hundred years earlier.
Jeffries' house is of faced stone, the other of mellow two-inch
brick ; otherwise they are very similar, with stone parapets,
sash windows framed in finely-moulded stone, shell porches
and a semi-circular flight of steps at the front door. The
stone house is still inhabited by a Jeffries, for the business,
which has been handed down from father to son for four

generations, is one of the very few of its kind which continue to prosper in these parts. Modern builders demand Oregon pine and red cedar instead of the stout timbers of English oak, which alone were strong enough to support the weight of stone tiles ; and as for fuel, even the rich burn more coal than wood nowadays. So most wood merchants turn colliers too, to make up on the roundabouts what they lose on the swings. Perhaps even here the time is not far off when the improvised trucks—grocery boxes on old perambulator wheels—crammed with their two-pennyworths of " strippings " will be trundled back to the cottage hearths for the last time, and the mosquito-like hum of the saw will be heard no longer. Most of all will be missed that familiar sight of the great timber wagon, drawn by three cart-horses, straining up the hill and rounding the corner of the lane as some still December day draws to a close, the clink and rattle of harness and the clod of hoofs sounding far along the road as the captive tree, lopped and in chains, is dragged home to its end.

These two Georgian houses marked the last of good building, though the school and schoolhouse might have been a good deal worse, especially considering that they went up in the year 1848. They are at least of good local stone, even if they seem anxious to be mistaken for churches and not many of their latticed windows will open. There had been a school of sorts before 1848 ; a small eighteenth-century charity had provided for " the Inftruction of Poore Children in Reading Writing and Arithmetick." The school teacher is supposed to have lived in Mrs. Keynes' cottage next to the pound ; she can show you the dunce's corner as proof positive. The first schoolmaster of the National School was paid sixteen pounds a year and had the schoolhouse rent-free; he also received the school pence which the children brought on Mondays. There were sixty children to be accommodated in two rooms, so an assistant teacher was engaged at half a crown a week. She had the harder task of keeping the younger ones in order. Now there are only thirty children; though, since their ages differ as widely as ever they did, it is just as hard to teach them. The reason for the fall in numbers is not entirely the declining birthrate. Buses and bicycles are now common, and it is an easy matter for children to attend the Senior School in the town if their parents so wish it. They often do, for the idea that town education and town occupations are superior to those of the country is slowly gaining hold. When this is " re-organised " as a Junior School with a headmistress it will be even more apparent that at the magic age of " eleven plus " one has outgrown village life. The change will mean, too, that the village will lose one of its most important figures—the schoolmaster. No woman, however capable and willing, can fill his place; there are so many tasks that fall to his share besides teaching. He can no longer be called scrivener-in-chief, for even old Joe Garlick can write his name if he takes long enough over it, but there are still occasions when the aid of a private secretary is sought. When, for instance, by some vagary of officialdom an income tax form found its way under Coffy Couzens' door, the only thing to do was to take it straight to Teacher Miles. This wiseacre was able to prevent the terrified Coffy from confessing not only to the five pounds he was saving towards the purchase of allotment land, but also to vaster sums which he did not possess at all. The schoolmaster is already organist, librarian, scoutmaster, secretary to the cricket club and clerk to the parish council; he must also audit the football club accounts, organise games at the children's Christmas party, plan Sunday school outings, advise a bewildered mother when her daughter refuses to go out to service, or tell Bill Comely what is the legal position if Farmer Drewett's ducks eat his broad beans.

Fifty years ago schoolmaster, doctor and parish priest together made the mental, physical and spiritual welfare of the village their care. There is no doctor now; ten years hence there may be no schoolmaster; but the little community is still fathered by its vicar. He is the sixtieth of an apostolic succession of incumbents beginning with the surnameless Robert, first recorded priest of the church of St. Giles. You may see the list of them in the church porch. Even the Reformation makes no apparent break in the chain, save that in the fifteen-forties the spiritual patron is exchanged for a temporal one—the King—as though it were of no more import than a change of raiment.

In 1834 the Ebenezer Baptist Chapel was erected. Its hermetically sealed windows of opaque green glass set high in its square walls make it look like a submarine prison. Another chapel—a Methodist one—was not slow in following. It is only just large enough to contain its handful of worshippers and its visiting lay preacher. Both chapels, despite their appearance, are warmly hospitable to the stranger in their midst. The Salvation Army in its early days thought the village godless enough in spite of its three places of worship, and made an attempt at converting it from the vantage point of Upper Common. The reception given to these pioneers showed that they had not been far wrong in their estimate. The young roughs immediately began, as they would have put it, to " create," for the tradition that these were people to be mocked and persecuted had spread as quickly as it had grown. Unquenched by their ducking in the pond that night, the Salvationists repeated their visit, and in the end, by reason of their importunity, they were suffered to meet unmolested in the disused cheese-room over the dairy at Church Farm.

Nineteenth-century architecture marred what had been till then an unspoilt village ; but the twentieth century did worse. Squire Everett's dictatorship had had one advantage —he had refused to allow telegraph posts to be planted on the common—not because he objected to their ugliness, for he had never considered whether they were ugly or not, but because he would tolerate no interference with what he considered his private property. So the chidden poles slunk across the farmers' fields, behind the churchyard, and so out to the main road. Four years ago, electricity threatened to rush in where the telephone had feared to tread. The question was brought up at a meeting of the parish council : should there be street lighting ? Since none of the village roads could be called a street, the quorum of six decided against it. But as to whether there should be electric light at all they were undecided. Miss Tarrant, who ran her own dynamo, considered it a waste of money. Mrs. Jeffries, who had recently allowed a paraffin lamp to flare up and ruin a freshly spring-cleaned room, would welcome a less smoky means of illumination. Obby (Albert) Hancock was fearful of the great forces pent up behind one little switch. " Cassn't thee follow I, you, unnerstand-zee," he argued, " wur be the Resistance ? 'E must bide zomewur, 'st-knaw ; wur be the

MASLIN FARM CHAPEL

Resistance ? " But as no one either followed, understood or saw, his exhortations fell on deaf ears. Teacher Miles was favourably inclined, but suggested that the cable should go underground : it would be safer, he said. (He was thinking of appearance rather than safety, but wisely decided that in present company it would prove the weaker argument.) George Knapp, Worthy Vines's grandson, was all for a well-lighted bar and a wireless such as his cousin in Calne had. Farmer Drewett said that what was good enough for his grandfather was good enough for him. Major Williamson, who might have given the casting vote, was away in Scotland. In the end, the poles and wires were admitted, with the proviso that they should be placed as inconspicuously as possible ; so the kindly elms along the lanes do their best to disguise them. But two miles from the market cross huge pylons stalk over the landscape like a file of skeleton invaders from another planet, sent to spy out the land.

Certain " modern amenities " came unobtrusively. Water has been laid on, chiefly for the benefit of the " foreigners " who have converted farms or built houses in this good hunting country. Most of the cottagers prefer their well water, which is not subject to the whims of a company who turn off the supply at the most inconvenient moment, and is softer for washing, colder for drinking. (Even if it is " condemned," past generations who drank it survived, so why should not they ?) When the telephone line was extended it was laid underground, and a kiosk was built. This has proved a white elephant ; on those very rare occasions when a villager needs to telephone a message or a wire he always gets Mrs. Comely to do it for him at the Post Office. He never minds her knowing his affairs. Here everyone knows everyone else's in any case, and Mrs. Comely, by the very nature of her office, is one from whom no secrets are hid. As she says, we all know that anyone who writes a postcard does not mind who reads it, and if she puts Miss Davenport through to the Nashes of an evening after dinner she cannot help but hear what they say, however hard she tries not to. So all that the till at the kiosk ever contains is two entrapped pennies abandoned there by some visitor ignorant of the Comely service, who pressed Button A too hastily and heard nothing but the " high-pitched buzz-buzz " for his pains.

Nearly every cottage, of course, is moored to its aerial mast, but as this is often an apple-tree or an extended clothes-post, and as there are nowhere more than six cottages together, the effect is not unsightly Now the same voice, speaking a tongue curiously remote from the Wessex speech of those into whose homes it intrudes, booms the same racing results from fifty open doorways, and the shepherd looks no longer to the sky but to the nightly forecast as his weather guide.

The village has its " hut," made of creosoted match-boarding and presented by the Co-operative Society in 1925. In its War Memorial it is more fortunate. In 1920 the remains of a preaching cross still stood in the churchyard, and the local mason was called upon to make a new shaft and cross for the old base. His work has never taken him farther afield than the villages and hamlets of the neighbourhood, but he knows his craft, no man better, and is incapable of doing a job otherwise than well. So the wash-house that he built on to the kitchen for his wife does not suffer by comparison with the handicraft of that other mason who made the house three hundred years before, and the memorial cross has been fashioned in the same tradition as the church in whose shadow it stands.

It is a pity that he was not asked to make the two bungalows—flimsy affairs with red roofs—at the Bramelham end of the village. There are not likely to be more of them, for this place is neither so renowned nor so conveniently situated as to attract week-end visitors or hordes of hikers; indeed, there is not so much as a cottage that " does " Teas, let alone Bed and Breakfast. To a person entering the village from Bramelham the two red spots look like fresh outbreaks of the plague he has left behind—the new Ideal Homes Estate, that creeps slowly countrywards, devouring trees and hedges as it goes.

But three and a half miles still feels a safe distance, and it is not the gradual encroaching of the town that is the greatest menace to peace. Five miles to the north there is a new military aerodrome. The village may be well off the main road, miles from the nearest railway station, so heavily screened by near and distant hedgerows that neither far town nor closest neighbour can be seen, but at any moment its privacy may be invaded from above and its silence violated by the angry grind of manoeuvring aeroplanes. " Us'll get used to thic rumpus," the people say resignedly. So they may—to the sound; but if they are to keep their old tranquillity of mind they must also get used to the knowledge that these swooping machines are practising the murder of other unknown villagers, who themselves are watching similar preparations for unknown, unhated foes. And why should they become used to the idea of destruction—the destruction of beauty, of quiet, or of fellow-creatures—here, where for a thousand years they have been used to seeing what is lovely, making things that will endure, and endeavouring to live together as friends ?

Part Two

THE CRAFTS OF THE VILLAGE

Thatching · Roadmending · Stone Walling
Hedging · Basket Making · Wagon Building · Gate-Making · Smithing

OF THOSE who still pursue the "mysteries" of the Middle Ages, Kington Borel can boast thatcher, mason, hedger, basketmaker, wheelwright, carpenter and smith.

All the thatching for many miles round—ricks, byres, sheds, walls, cottages, dovecotes—is the work of Joseph Gingell, who lives in the cottage next to Church Farm. Although he is over seventy he sets out in all weathers, pushing his trucks that contain his stock-in-trade—the twine and the withy-bonds that hold the thatch in position, the twisted hazel " spicks " for pegging them down, and his few simple tools. He needs a large pointed knife for sharpening spicks ; a barge knife like a slightly straightened reap-hook for trimming eaves ; a long iron rod, hooked at one end and pointed at the other, for negotiating places beyond easy reach ; a thick, short oaken bat for beating down the thatch ; and a wooden comb with sparse curved teeth for raking smooth the " yelms " or bundles of cornstraw. The handle of this tool ends in a sharp point which can pierce the thatch before the spicks are thrust in. With the exception of the knives, these are home-made implements, designed with the efficiency of the maker who knows his requirements.

The Gingells' cottage is an old thatched one ; there is no ornament at the ridge, but along the eaves runs a kind of herring-bone pattern, about a foot in width, formed by two intersecting zig-zag lines of withy between two straight rows.

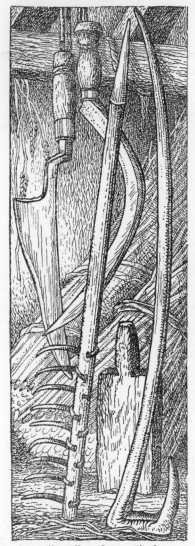

The Thatcher's Tools.

Wherever the withy-bonds meet or cross they are fastened with a spick. At the side of the roof the thatch is made secure with a few transverse bands of withy. The thatcher reckons that a roof needs to be renewed every ten years, and for a cottage like this his charge is about ten pounds. Here no-one uses wire netting to protect the thatch from marauding sparrows and starlings; so thick are the layers of straw that a patch of new yelm now and again is usually sufficient to repair the damage. This cottage and garden are almost unbelievably picturesque and trim, but the neatness is that of the craftsman who must find his materials in good condition and ready to hand, and quaintness is inevitable when everything that can be thatched is thatched—roof, garden wall, winch, and even the henhouse. At the back of the cottage is a pile of hazel faggots leaning up against the "hovel" where the bundles of spicks are kept. The name has no derogatory connotation, but means simply—what it looks like—a little house. The heap of ready-combed yelms has itself been thatched, even though it will soon be dismembered again.

THE CRAFTS OF THE VILLAGE

The busiest time of year for Joseph Gingell is August and September, when there are ricks to be thatched. The hayrick is usually shaped like a house, with a plain ridged roof. The tops of the cornricks are conical, and the peaks are sometimes ornamented with a few twists of straw, or a pile of straw coils like a small bee skep, or a tuft of unthreshed ears or a straw bird. Nowadays these are made because they have always been made, or because the artist in straw finds joy in his work, but the custom has its origin in the heathen rites connected with the reaping of the last sheaf of corn. The bunch of full ears, and probably the pigeon-like effigy, are propitiatory offerings to the bird enemy. Hereabouts the commonest finial is a simple crown made of four straw plaits

Joseph Gingell's Cottage.

65

looped round a central stake. The rick finials at Priory Farm are of this kind, but more elaborate. They are like weather-vanes, the crown surmounting a foundation of two crossed sticks, twined and bound together with straw and frayed into fans at the four ends. The ricks will be undone for threshing

Rick Ornaments.

in February. No matter ; the farmer feels it is worth the trouble that for twenty weeks or so his eyes should be continually satisfied with the dignity of these dozen crowns that mark the ricks as his own : they spell good husbandry, craftsmanship, prosperity, even luxury—the luxury of work done for joy and not for need.

Joseph Gingell has taught his trade to his son, but it is doubtful whether Ted will be like his father, hale and weather-beaten, proud of his work and enjoying it, at threescore and ten. The present bye-law forbids the thatching of new houses ; it is easier to enforce this than to insist that chimneys be swept at least twice a year and that couch fires be burnt at a safe distance from the house, though every inhabitant of a thatched cottage takes this for granted. And Joseph started work before the use of corrugated iron became general. Of this material, hideous in texture and in colour alike, are made the Dutch barns which are gradually ousting both granary and rick ; sometimes, to add insult to injury,

Rick Ornaments.

it replaces the weathered stone tiles which have been stripped from fine old roofs to grace new " restorations " in distant parts, and the cottager in need of a garden shed builds of it a " hovel " that is a hovel indeed. Fortunately, seventeenth-century cottages were built to last, and there are many thatched ones in the villages of north-west Wiltshire. Yet Ted Gingell may think twice before making his son a thatcher.

Along the Stanley Fitzurse road works one who is also of a vanishing race—the roadmender, Daniel Beak. He is a queer little hump-backed man, with a mask like a highwayman's over his eyes, and he moves his pitch from heap to heap of the white limestone by the roadside, breaking it small and filling it into the hollows made by cartwheels in wet weather. For this road is seldom used by cars, and has not lost its original white paving. A white lane is one of the most beautiful sights of the passing English country. In spring it is like a path prepared for a bride, with may blossom in either hedge and feathery cow-parsley lining the grass verges ; in summer the tall elms cast across it cool, heavy shadows that are the more welcome after the stretches of dazzling brightness. In late autumn its creamy mud is inlaid with a mosaic of leaves—flaming maple, spotted sycamore, russet oak, golden elm and dark ash : on a frosty winter night it is silver everywhere, from the rimy trees that flank it to the hard ruts skimmed over with ice. The stone by the main roadside is blue-grey granite, some in coarse lumps, some broken small so that it looks like a slag-heap ; near by lie the tar barrels. The navy blue of the finished road consorts well with the steel of pylons and the shining flash of cars : beside mellow thatch and stone, ancient trees and flowering hedge-rows it can never look otherwise than alien.

Daniel Beak makes good roads, but he is not a connoisseur in his material like Bob Wilkins the mason, who knows as soon as he handles a stone what purpose it will serve. He it is who makes the stone stiles that lead from field to field. The simplest is a single mighty slab, but it is usually provided with steps like a mounting-block ; one, two or three on either side. Some stiles are of the kind here called " squeeze-belly," though these are more often of wood. A stone squeeze-belly is merely a narrow V-shaped gap between two large slabs. To get through, a man turns his body sideways and raises himself slightly on tiptoe ; a grazing animal is effectually kept on its own side of the wall.

But the mason's chief work is the making of the stone walls that are frequently used to divide field or copse from roadside, or to surround a cottage garden. They are built without mortar, their construction rendering them sufficiently secure. The foundation trench is a foot deep and two feet wide. The stones, which are quarried from the surface,

A stone wall in the making.

are carefully chosen for their size and shape, and are laid with the more even edges facing outwards and the rougher edges facing together, the odd spaces between being filled with rubble. Each course slopes slightly downwards from the centre, and is so laid that the joins do not coincide with those of the course below. Occasionally a " spear " stone is set across the width of the wall to tie the whole structure. The top course of " comers " is only one foot six inches wide, the gradual decreasing from the foundation being arrived at by working to a wooden template as the wall proceeds in sections. As a rule the coping is a row of " cock-ups," but where a more finished appearance is required, as, for example, round the churchyard wall, flat slabs are used, and garden walls are sometimes rounded off with mortar which soon acquires a growth. Sawmills Lane has on its north side a " haha " wall—the top is level with the field. This kind is particularly rich in vegetation—ivy, herb Robert, shining cranesbill, ivy-leaved toadflax, white dead nettle and pellitory of the wall.

Only rarely here are stone walls found separating fields, as in the neighbouring county. Cobbett, travelling in Gloucestershire, could not endure them : " Anything quite so cheerless as this I do not recollect to have seen ; . . . these stones are quite abominable." Unforgivable though his blindness to their beauty is, a landscape of hedgerows is perhaps more welcoming, less bare—if the hedges are well kept. In Kington Borel only Simeon Robbins of Priory Farm and the Freeths of Maslin Farm continue to have their hedges cut and laid. The other farmers say they cannot afford it, and in their fields every year the sturdy growth of the spring and summer is ruthlessly hacked down, and the shards are roughly filled with some of the hedge cuttings. So Charlie Cole, who works for Simeon Robbins, is one of the few men in the village who still know something of

A Simple Stone Stile.

hedging. Since a hedge should be cut and laid at least once in every five years, there are several to be done every winter, and he usually starts in January. During the intervening years they must be topped, and this is done in the autumn. There are two distinct kinds of hedge in the village : one, like that in Long Summers, entirely of hawthorn and quite straight, showing that it was made at the time of the later Enclosures, the other (by far the commoner in this village) curved, and planted with a mixed growth of hazel, wych elm, holly, elder, dogwood, buckthorn, spindle, sloe, privet, wayfaring tree, guelder rose, crab apple and maple. These are the older hedges, and the curve facilitated the turning of the plough at the headland. In Great Lynch, the right of way to the farm at Mount Pleasant follows this wavy line of hedge—a more convenient arrangement than a bee-line across in a field like this, where wheat, turnips and oats are grown in succession. Charlie Cole, of course, knows all the fields by name—curious names like Upper and Lower Sams, Crip and Go, Coppershell, Dallydown Rails and Lounces Leases, and names to which time has given a poetry unsuspected by

A Stone "Squeeze-belly."

those who first gave the fields, for purely practical reasons, their distinguishing descriptions—Sheeps Sleight, Goosey Acre, Driftway, Broad Furlong, Tithe Platts, Parsons Ground, No Notion, Long Summers, and French Field (which because of its triangular shape was ploughed in a "French gore") and Roundabouts, almost encompassed by Brimble Copse. Whether the field is his especial care or no, his watchful eye has noted the gaps in its defences. It is an education to watch him at work. A less skilful hand than his would slash off the branches: he knows just how and how far to bring his billhook down slantwise through the stem so that it can be bent over. The finished hedge looks like basket-work: the branches lie neatly all one way, so close that not even a hen could squeeze through at the bottom; the upright stakes hold them now in front, now behind, and the top is finished with a pleaching of hazel "edders."

You would know Abel Wootton's thatched cottage for a basketmaker's some way off, because of the stacks of reddish-brown willow that are propped against the wall and the wooden shed where he works. It stands by the Bever-bourne, and on its banks, where the "withibed" of the Saxon charter stood, he grows his withies. There is always some of his handiwork to be seen outside the back door: a circular basket for the dog, an ancient beehive chair, a carrier on the old bicycle, a covered egg-basket near the chicken-run, a clothes basket piled high with Mrs. Wootton's snowy washing, or the baby's willow cradle on rockers. At one end of the shed are the finished orders—hampers and

A Stone Stile with steps, leading to Priory Farm.

bushel and shopping baskets to sell in the market, chaff baskets and corn servers for farmers, or venison baskets, destined for Scotland, awaiting the railway van. Some are of unpeeled willow, some of white; others are reddish— " buffed ", Abel calls them. These are the baskets that must be made with special care, for only the best withy is buffed. The colour is obtained by boiling the wands for twelve hours and straightway peeling them, by which time the bark has impregnated the wood beneath with its own dye. But, pleasant though the colour is, it does not bear comparison with the rich natural beauty of the unpeeled willow, that is here orange, there olive green.

73

Baskets are as old as the need for them ; they were made before east was east and west was west, by peoples living too far apart to learn the art from one another ; each individually evolved its own tradition, yet whatever the material it is fundamentally the same tradition the world over. The patterns Abel Wootton uses were taught him by his father, who in his turn learnt them by making them as a young apprentice—the oval gardening basket, the cylindrical lidded hamper, the shapely log-basket like a double coal-scuttle that can be loaded at either end, and, most beautiful of all, the basket-of-all-trades, a simple brown hemisphere, its only ornament the contrasting white willow in a band near the

A Wooden " Squeeze-belly."

rim and for the base and handle. There are two kinds of baskets he never makes now : one is the wicker container for the flagon that held the harvesters' ale or cider ; the other is the long sheath attached to the back of a pony-trap to hold the large umbrella. The last umbrella basket was made by

Abel's father for Mr. and Mrs. Freeth of Maslin Farm, who might have been seen journeying to and from market beneath the shelter of the faded green gamp right up to the time when the younger generation of Freeths became of an age to object to anything so old-fashioned.

The only part of Abel's work that is done out of doors is the cutting and preparing of the withies. They are cut in December and are laid in water in a trough till the end of May or the beginning of June, when those that are to make white baskets are ready to be peeled. Very occasionally they are seasoned earlier ; if they are peeled too late they develop a second skin which flakes and causes trouble in the weaving. The peeling is done by rubbing each withy between two iron spikes driven through a log. In Abel's log there are two sets of these spikes ; they go back to the time when he worked side by side with his father. The old man now helps but seldom, and Abel carries on the trade alone, for nowadays, when the milk, bacon and butter factories pay a young man thirty shillings a week, no-one is willing to serve an apprenticeship to a craft as Abel's father served his, nor to take the risk and responsibility of setting up in business on his own afterwards.

A good supply of both peeled and unpeeled withies is carried into the shed and is put where Abel can easily reach them as he sits on his cushion on the boarded floor. Close at hand are his tools—knives of various shapes, pincers, two or three " bodkins " that start near the handle as three-cornered files and end like stilettos, and most important of all, a tool called the beating-iron, rather like a thick, flat shoe-horn. Like some of the thatcher's tools, this beater serves many purposes and is needed for almost every process ; but

75

its chief use corresponds with that of the weaver's beater—it presses down each row of weft as it is finished, to make the fabric firm and level.

Rick Ornaments at Priory Farm.

Anyone seeing, for the first time, a bushel basket begun would think that some mystic ritual was being performed. Abel cuts five short sticks of withy, pares their middles to make a slightly flattened surface, and then lays them on the ground before him in the form of a cross, two sticks over three sticks. To keep them in position he stands on the arms of the cross, then bows himself to the earth and lays a rod of withy beside the two upper sticks. This is his " slew " or weaving withy, and he passes it under, over, under, over

76

the centre of his cross till he has bound it firmly. Then, rising, he separates the arms of the cross into a star with eleven spokes, and, resuming his bent position, he introduces a second " slew." With the pair of them he weaves round the spokes, one slew in front, one behind ; one behind, one

Abel Wootton's shed.

in front, all the while holding down one spoke at a time firmly with his left foot and pulling up its farther end, so making a saucer-shaped wheel. He does not stand upright till he has finished his " slaught," and at this stage it looks

77

like a half-finished spider's web. It takes a small man, he says, to be a basket-maker; his father is a small man, too. No-one with long legs would find slaught-making comfortable. Now he sits on his cushion with his working-board, propped at one end to make it slope, on his legs. On this he places his slaught, with a weight in its centre to keep it firm, and proceeds to " fill up the bottom," that is, to complete the base of the basket.

The next job is the " staking-up." He turns the bottom convex side uppermost, and with his knife he sharpens the butt ends of some stakes five or six feet long, and drives them into the spaces between the spokes and the inter-sections of the slews. The radius of his wheel is now the length of a withy, and at this stage he sometimes requires so much room that he has to continue working outside the shed till he has finished the next process, the " upsetting "; that is, the turning of these long withies at right angles to form the framework of the basket. He makes a small incision in each stake where he wants his bend to be, and now the iron ring that is the handle of his beater comes into play. He slips each withy in turn through it and cracks it at the incision as one would a nut, so that it easily turns up verti-cally. (This ring can be used to set as well as to break sticks : it is needed to straighten those that form the framework of the tops of hampers.) To keep the upright withies or " struts " in position the basket-maker slips over them a hoop made of twisted cane ; then he weaves with his deft, strong hands, using two or three withies to each slew, till his basket is the required height. New bonds must be intro-duced at different points in the round so that the weaving may keep level ; and the spaces between the struts must be constantly regulated lest a " spout " should be formed by two or three struts falling together. Square baskets, too, present their difficulties. The struts tend to lean in one direction, and to counteract this they must be given a definite bias in the opposite direction as the weaving proceeds. Abel's father was expert at contriving this balance ; his square baskets were true to a quarter of an inch.

Next, the border must be plaited. Five of the struts are cracked with the beater and are turned horizontally to lie along the rim ; those remaining are bent over by hand. When the handles have been affixed and the rough ends trimmed with a " picking knife " the basket is finished. It takes Abel half an hour to make such a one, and he sells it for one and sixpence wholesale or two shillings to private customers ; a price which takes no account of the time spent in cutting, soaking, stripping and preparing the withies, nor of the long years of practice required before the eyes and hands are sufficiently skilled to keep the slope of the sides regular and the circle true.

In the same way, how much trial and error on the part of nameless generations of wheelwrights has gone to the making of one of Benjamin Brinkworth's wagons, that are built not in spite of but because of the quality and behaviour of the timber, the windings and narrowness of country lanes, the unevenness of fields, the shape and gait and strength of a horse, and the weight and nature of the loads to be carted. Benjamin Brinkworth's work is concerned mostly with the repairing and, less often, with the making of farm wagons and tradesmen's carts—haywains, dung-carts, milkfloats, bakers' vans and the like. His uncle, from whom he learnt

Wiltshire Hoop-raved Wagon.

the trade, used to make wooden ploughs also, but he himself
has not so much as repaired one since he took over the
business, for iron ploughs are now generally used. He still
possesses two of his uncle's make, however. One is a breast-
plough—the plough reduced to its lowest terms, handle and
coulter, and resembling nothing so much as a huge long-
handled trowel. Joe Garlick remembers digging the stubble
of Parsons Ground with one such plough, he pushing and
Will Clapp pulling with a rope. The other is an old Wiltshire
foot plough, which was never sold, and Ben kept it, first as
a pattern, if need should arise, then out of sentiment. It is
a primitive-looking implement, such as may be seen in the
illustrations of many a mediæval manuscript, but in grace of
line it is gallant as a boat. Indeed, like the great wagons,

Old Wiltshire Foot Plough.

it was built to ride the rough fields as a ship rides the seas. The curving beam, finely chamfered, and the twisted shelboard were sawn each from a single log that the ploughwright's practised eye had selected as apt for his purpose. The iron plough in comparison looks a poor starveling.

Of all the wagons that come into the wheelwright's yard for repairs, Simeon Robbins' three-ton haywain is the king. Once no more remarkable than others of its kind, it is now unique in the neighbourhood. Ben takes a proprietary interest in it, for it was made by his grandfather for Simeon Robbins' father, who paid thirty-eight pounds for it. It is a Wiltshire hoop-raved or bow-raved wagon; that is, the " rave " or surboard continues from the front wheel and rises in a curve over the back wheel, which is higher. The shape of the wagon, side view, is (like that of the plough) so graceful that one would imagine the curve to have been made for beauty's sake alone. In fact, however, this and all the other less obvious curves of the wagon—for scarcely a timber of it is straight—were born of necessity, and each necessity was born of another. The wagon bed was limited

81

to three feet ten inches in width ; the addition of raves would extend its carrying capacity by sixteen inches at either side. The width of the bed was determined by the width of the wheel-track (in this case five feet eight inches), which had to depend on the distance between the ruts in the road. The continual come-and-go of carts of the traditional width had made those ruts, and they in turn, since they could not be altered save by road engineering unheard of a century ago, perpetuated the tradition. The rave rose in a curve because front and back wheels were of unequal height, the front wheels being three feet ten inches, the back wheels a foot wider in diameter. For this, too, there was a reason. The higher the wheels the better would hubs and " exes " (axles) clear the mire of those rough roads : the lower the front wheels, the more easily would the wagon lock in a narrow turning-space. To be sure, the rave could have been made high enough from the ground to clear the back wheels throughout its length ; but in that case the carter would have had to raise his load well over five feet to get it into the wagon. The rave, therefore, followed the curve of the wheels, and the carter loads at the " waist " of the wagon, where the rave is lowest—four feet nine inches high. The bed is made slightly lower here than at front and back, to distribute the weight of the load. It is also two inches narrower at the waist than at the back, so that the front wheels can lock further without becoming jammed on the body as they turn. The " dish " of the wheels—their marked tilt outwards—helps this, too, and at the same time corrects the thrust of the load.

How much bitter experience must have gone to the growth of wagon-building ! How many parts were made

Front view of the Wagon.

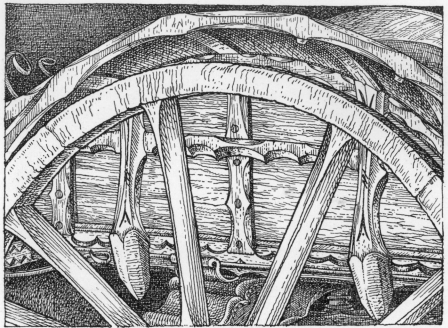

The Hoop-rave, showing strouters.

of the wrong kind of wood before it was decreed that hubs should be of heart of elm or oak (according to the quality of the local timber), shafts of ash, spokes of oak? How often was the work made of none account because the wood was full of knots or " shakes " or had been imperfectly seasoned? What wagons were made too heavy to be drawn, too cumbersome to turn, too wide for their lanes, too casually put together to stand the strain imposed on them? To the many failures and perseverances of those workmen of the past the wheelwright of to-day owes the lore of the craft he practises, sometimes without consciously realising the why and the wherefore of what he does, but knowing only that it can be done that way and no other.

Nor is it in the general shape and construction alone that

the slow building up of the tradition is apparent : it shows as surely in the smallest detail. There is not a harsh line in the whole wagon. Throughout, the angles have been softened, the thicknesses tapered, and, as with the shape of the rave, the beauty of these curves is inevitable rather than consciously artistic. The finished wagon, built as stoutly as need required, was over-heavy, and to lighten the frame all surplus wood was gouged away with the " draw-shave "—no more than a chamfer here and a nick there ; but in this way over two hundredweight could be removed (one-ninth of the entire weight) without loss of strength. Hence the beautiful scoops and scallops to be found, not only in the parts more easily seen, like the edges of the raves, the shutlocks and the strouters (the wooden buttresses that strengthen the sides), but also in the hidden parts, and notably in the under-carriages beneath the wagon-bed. The shaving had to be done, but it was an artist who did it : the wood must be removed, but he knew just where and how to remove it ; and when it came to the painting he could not refrain here and there from one touch more than sheer need demanded, tracing the outline of his finished carvings, and inscribing on the front of the wagon, besides the name of its owner and the date of making, a few scrolls and flourishes and floral patterns in keeping with the contemporary handwriting.

Simeon Robbins' wagon is yellow picked out in red, though most of his other carts are blue with red wheels. It bears on its headboard the date 1851, though none of its kind was considered worthy to stand with the pompous furniture and ornate bric-a-brac chosen to represent the art level of England at the Great Exhibition that year. Indeed, had this very wagon been selected as an exhibit no-one would have

thought the choice more improper than Amos Brinkworth :
he counted himself no artist, but a simple wheelwright.

The headboard is keel-shaped ; and resting idly on its un-
harnessed shafts the wagon does look rather like a stranded
boat. All along the fore-shutlock is a row of zig-zag carving
akin to the Norman hatched chevron ornament. Below this

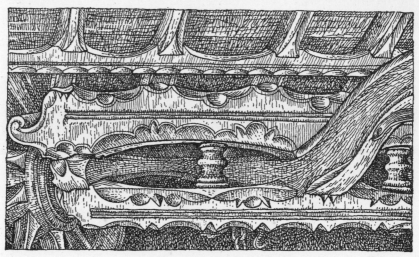

A portion of the hind-carriage.

show the ends of the wagon-blades and the summers, the
main timbers supporting the bed throughout its length. Like
all projecting members these are chamfered and faceted into
blunt points. In the gloom beneath them the fore-carriage or
" hound " can be dimly seen. It is one of the most beautiful
parts of the wagon. The subtle curves of the transverse
pieces and the finely-turned spindles do the work of springs.
The hind-carriage is as exquisitely shaped and carved, with
repeating groups of scallops and straight bands of beading.

It is not surprising that the wheelwright earned his name
from his skill in making one particular part of the wagon.

The fashioning of the wheels is an art in itself. The process stretches over years, from the first selecting, sawing and rough-hewing of the timber to be seasoned to the tyring at the smithy. The business of fitting the twelve spokes into the stock at the shoulder end, and at the other end into the six " vellies " that together make the circle (two spokes to each " velly "), then the dowelling of the vellies together in such a way as to allow for the contraction caused by the cooling of the encircling tyre—these would be delicate matters enough of themselves, but to complicate them further there is the dish of the wheel to be reckoned with, affecting the angles at which the spokes are to be driven into stock and vellies, and there is the angle of the dish itself, which will be slightly exaggerated in the shrinking. On the wheel more than on any other part of the wagon the draw-shave is used, and after it the spoke-shave, to pare away all wood that can possibly be dispensed with. The spoke is originally a rectangular block, but the chamfers on either side of the front face are made so wide as almost to meet in the middle. Near the ends, however, where spoke meets velly and stock and extra strength is required, the chamfer vanishes in a fine curve and the spoke resumes its full width. The inside of the wheel has to stand the weight of the load as it is swayed outwards with the movement of the horse's body, so on its inner surface the spoke is merely rounded. Benjamin Brinkworth always cuts his initials on the foot of the spoke so that when the time eventually comes for the wheel to be dismembered for repairs and the foot is withdrawn from the stock he can recognise his work.

This is a wagon made for double shafts or "thills," as they are sometimes called. The two inner shaft poles are therefore rather straighter, to allow of the horses coming closer together ; the outer poles follow more nearly the curve of a horse's body, wider at the back than at the front. The cross timbers of these shafts, like those of the under-carriages, are joined by spindles instead of solid bars of wood, thus combining strength with lightness ; for the same reason the shafts are cunningly tapered towards the ends. Benjamin's last repair was to turn some more spindles for them, for it goes without saying that many a new part has been made since Amos Brinkworth gave the wagon its finishing touches. In those days, fixed to the hames of each horse were " boxbells "—a set of four latten bells, made by that famous eighteenth-century Wiltshire bell-founder, Robert Wells of Aldbourne, and inscribed with his initials. There are two bells hanging in the dairy now, though one has lost its cruciform clapper. The black leather canopy, ornamented with brass studs, under which they hung has long since disappeared. Together the bells sounded the common chord, whose music gave warning of the coming of the team along the narrow lanes. The old wagon is still used for haymaking and harvest, but the day cannot be far off when even Simeon Robbins will decide that it must go to the wheelwright's yard for the last time.

In wagon-making, balance, proportion and economy of construction are seen at their best, but every craft in some degree reveals these qualities, for without any one of them nothing can be made well. Man's recognition of the character of wood is shown in the humble gate as well as in the lordly wain, and here, too, the lore of an age-old craft is modified to become the tradition of a locality. There is a Wiltshire

A double gate slat.

wagon, and there are Wiltshire gates—one might say there are Kington Borel gates, for a few miles beyond the village the pattern changes, and one is forced to the conclusion that those within this small radius were the work of one craftsman.

Benjamin Brinkworth can make and has made gates, but to-day by mutual consent it is Jim Gosling who supplies the demand. He is the village undertaker, but as a death is a rare occurrence in Kington Borel this business is not brisk, and Benjamin, having as much as he can do at his workshop (in spite of the degenerate substitution, here and there, of motor tyres for the fine old wooden cartwheels), leaves it to Joe to do the outside jobs.

All the local five-barred gates are of oak, weathered to a lichen grey. They are nearly ten feet long, and are strengthened by one diagonal brace and two upright slats, one down the middle of the gate, the other equidistant from the middle and the " head " or " falling-post "—that is, the latch end. Sometimes these slats are single bars through which the rails pass, sometimes they are in two parts, one on either side of the rails. The proportions of these gates are so familiar and at the same time so satisfying that to see one of a less comely pattern—one, for instance, in which the five rails are spaced with mathematical regularity—is to experience a shock.

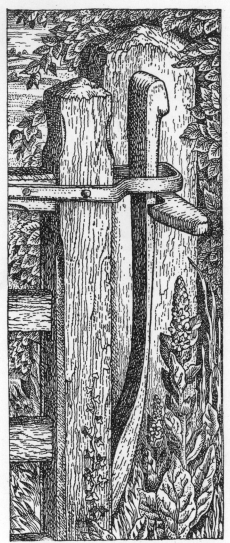

A gate " harr," with burdock growing near.

An oak gate and staple catch, with great mullein growing near.

The post nearest the hinge—called by the Saxon name of the hinge itself, the " harr "—is of a particular shape. The square top ends in a low pyramid. Just below the top rail the harr swells out with a handsome moulding, then curves in towards the waist, and narrows into a square post at the bottom, the transition being marked by a small gouged pattern. This extra thickness at the hinge end ensures that the gate will open easily without undue strain and will stay open when required ; and, as on the finished wagon, the draw-shave is used, not only on the harr, but on the whole gate, to reduce the weight to the minimum, so that every bar is lightly chamfered at every angle. This smoothing of corners incidentally makes the gate much more pleasant to handle.

Whatever the word may mean, the " hlypgeat " or " leap-gate " was commoner in these parts, according to the early charters, than the " hlidgeat " or swing-gate. Perhaps, where deer and cattle grazed, the deer leapt the fences that confined the cattle ; maybe the gate had a step or a stile so that men could " leap " over rather than swing it open. The gate

Cookrow Gate.

An iron gate catch and staple.

leading into the Cookrow fields has one lower rail extended widthwise into a step on either side—a good idea where cattle are grazing and passers-by using the footpath are not too vigilant in shutting gates. As if this were not enough precaution, it has in addition a wooden squeeze-belly at the side. There is one also at the top of White Stocking Lane, its sides worn to a high polish by the constant brushing through of villagers on their way to and from Allenford.

The gate fastenings vary. Some gates lift to open; a few that lead into private copses in hunting country can be opened by the rider, who without dismounting depresses the spring catch with his hunting crop. Some latch as a door does; others are secured by a hasp that passes over a staple and is held in place by a peg. But most gates here have a long catch, usually of oak, though occasionally of ash, thickened and shaped at the top to give it a comfortable grip, and at the bottom where it

92

joins the " head," and tapered thinly in the middle. This makes a strong spring so that the gate will fit securely into its wooden catch staple, and will even shut of its own accord when pushed. This catch and its staple may be of iron instead of wood, for the smith has a good deal to do with gate-making. An iron catch ends at the top in a curl like that of a shepherd's crook, or in a round or many-faceted knob, and at the bottom is beaten out into a flat heart-shaped flange that can be nailed to the head. Sometimes the staple is given a few spiral twists before it, too, is beaten into a shapely finish.

The hinges also are smith's work. They consist of a " gate-hook," which is driven into the gate-post, and a thick ring to slip over the hook, called a " thimble," which is fixed to the harr. To strengthen the hinge, the thimble is extended into a " wing " of iron which is nailed along the rail of the gate. Some wings, like the spring catches, taper into a heart shape, others are finished with a pattern of vertical grooves. Nails are used only to fasten iron to wood ; where slat or brace crosses rail hand-made wooden dowels are driven in, while the rails are fixed into the head and harr and the slats and brace into the rails by mortice and tenon joints.

When the entrance to the field is on a slope, Henry Hazell, who does all the ironwork required for Jim Gosling's gates, often has to make a weight and chain that will pull the gate to ; then the carter need not leave the horse in order to shut it. These chains are forged of cunningly twisted double links, each connected not only with the link immediately preceding, but with the link before that.

Henry Hazell and Benjamin Brinkworth have each only

A gate " harr" with weight and chain, and showing iron thimble and wing.

one assistant. In the past smith, wheelwright and carpenter must have employed more labour, and even then must have been very fully occupied. There was so much more to be made—heddles and shuttles and pedals for looms, perhaps, once upon a time, and, not so very long ago, pattens and wooden flails. Polly Fry at the Almshouses still wears pattens when she goes across the fields on wet days, and Joe Garlick could wield the flail when he was a lad on the farm at Stanley Fitzurse. He called it a " drashel," and " flail " was his name for the beater. It was made of good hard yew, while the staff was of ash, and they were tied by an intricate knot of eel-skin. Threshing was skilled labour if you were to avoid hitting your partner, but it was hard, and the threshing machine must have been a welcome innovation. There were shepherds' crooks to be forged, and winches and pumps to be made with their handles and chains. The buckets were the work of the cooper, who made also the barrels, bung-casks, rainwater vats and washtubs for domestic use— a barrel sawn in half made two excellent washtubs. The goffering iron that Polly Fry used for " getting up " her sunbonnets, the finely-wrought iron sign at the White Hart, the quoits the villagers threw on the common, were the smith's handiwork. The carpenter fashioned the great wooden rakes used for collecting hay, and cut the well-crooks for the women who had no menfolk to do it for them. Presumably it was he who made those now obsolete tools—the " fiddle " for broadcasting seed, and the sieve for strewing sand on the floor at the time when this was a daily, and sometimes a twice-daily, household task. Swings and see-saws (" weigh-jolts," as Kington people call them) were joint productions. To be sure, the carpenter alone could have turned out these—a swing need be no more than a board cleft for the rope to pass through, and a weigh-jolt but a plank balanced across a log. But safer far, if less exciting, were the weigh-jolt firmly bolted in the centre and the swing that hung by mighty iron hooks. The Freeths, who yearly entertain the Baptist Sunday School children at Maslin Farm, have the strongest of strong swings hanging from a beam in their big barn, and in Chapel Ground the most secure of see-saws.

Henry Hazell is up at four, for there is always a good day's work ahead. There will be no need for him to take to selling petrol and doing bicycle repairs, as some smiths in other villages have done. Shoeing alone occupies much of his time, for there are hunters as well as farm horses to be shod. When a pony requires its first pair of shoes he goes to the stable to take the measurements. A pony can wear out its shoes in three weeks, and the smith always has in readiness a set to fit each of his horse customers. Trotting shoes must

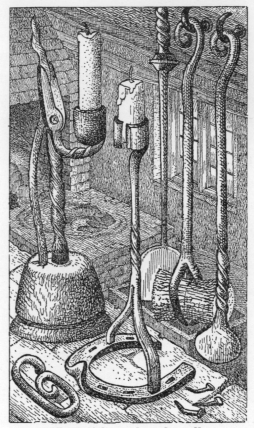

The Smith's tools and candles.

be wide in the web, though not so wide as the ancient shoes, which covered so much of the hoof that little of the " frog " (the soft, inner part) could be seen. Hunters' shoes, on the other hand, are narrow and grooved, with specially con-structed " heels " on the hind shoes. They cost ten shillings the set, while a set for a farm horse costs eight shillings. Gone are the days when the charge was two and eightpence —cheap enough for the iron, the labour of making the four shoes to measurement, and the job of removing the old set, paring the hoofs, and fitting the new shoes.

Half of the smithy is like a stable, without stalls but with iron rings in the walls to which the horses can be tied. From the beam above hang innumerable sets of shoes, from huge carthorses' to small ponies'. This is a very different place from Joe Gingell's neat home. There is no apparent order in Henry Hazell's piles of ironwork, yet he himself knows exactly where to lay his hand on everything that is required —and shoes, at least, are wanted in a hurry. Jinny Freeth, the mare that draws the milkfloat, will soon require hers, and Prince Drewett is already overdue for his ; they are designed to counteract his tendency to kick himself when trotting. The village animals are known by name, and they usually take their masters' surnames. Kington Borel has many familiar characters such as " Voilet " Beak, the roadmender's goat that he tethers by the wayside, and George Freegard, the old sheepdog at Allenford Farm. The smith has good reason for knowing the horses individually: they are his patients as well as his clients. He is often called up in the dead of night to attend to some sick animal ; and his veterinary skill lends so much authority to the advice on herbal remedies for human ailments which he freely dispenses at the smithy that no-one dares to object that the cure is worse than the disease when he is bidden, for instance, to rub his tonsils with pepper as a cure for tonsilitis.

In the centre of the smithy is the forge, with its flat hearth on one side of the huge brick chimney and its leathern bellows on the other. A small red fire glows on the hearth. From time to time Henry replenishes it with a shovelful of slack. The shovel is hand made, as are all his tools. They show his resource and ingenuity—his recognition of the end desired and the most economical and efficient means of achieving it. Here is a small wide borax spoon ; the end of its long handle curls into a hook by which it can hang, and towards the head it is twisted, for this is one of those good old tools that serve a double purpose—the spiral part of the handle is used as a file. In the trough of water at the end of the hearth is a " swop," a small bundle of rushes fixed in an iron handle. This is dabbed on to the heated iron when it requires cooling ; it also comes in handy for scattering the crowd of small boys whose curiosity draws them within the half-door and too near the forge. On its massive wooden block stands the anvil, its beak pointed towards the hearth. Close by are ranged other things that must lie ready to hand : the tripod on which the horse rests its hoof while being shod ; hammers, chisels, nails, punches, drills, tongs and pincers of various shapes and sizes, and an implement so necessary that it is called simply " the tool," or sometimes, because it is a good substitute for a second pair of hands, " the boy." This is a rough iron gauge that can hold the tongs in three different positions. Another improvisation is the " axo " (hack-saw), a piece of an old scythe with one edge toothed so that it can be used for cutting iron. Occasionally, especially if it be winter, darkness falls before work is done, and light is needed. So the smith makes himself candlesticks of the material available. The candle needs a sconce ; it must have a stem long enough to throw the light down ; so thus it is made. The stem has to be set in a firm, well-weighted base. What could be better than a good heavy horse-shoe, with nail-holes already made for sockets ? Or there is an old rushlight holder, that only needs a candle sconce to make it once more a useful means of illumination.

In the home as well as in the smithy his eye is quick to

see what is needed and how the need can be supplied.
Shovels, tongs, pokers, fenders and firedogs ; garden
railings, door-scrapers, latches—these Mrs. Hazell might
expect a smith-husband to provide ; but his inventive mind
helps her also in more domestic affairs : he makes her nut-
crackers, or a toasting-fork, or an iron collar to keep the
draught from her oil stove.

Hanging on the walls or the beams of the smithy or lying
in odd corners the most interesting assortment of articles
may be found ; some finished, some awaiting repair, some
degraded to scrap-iron. Here are odd parts from chaff-
cutting machines, the " tines " of harrows or a delicately-
curled shepherd's crook ; there gate-irons, a whippletree and
a paddle from a plough ; and everywhere chains—chains to
fasten cows into their stalls, gate-chains, chains for the
" drags," " rollers " and tailboards of carts. Outside among
the rusty heap of shoes are some old field-forks. No two are
alike. This was a hayfork, with the graceful curve of cows'
horns, and designed for much the same purpose—for tossing ;
and this small one was a beating-prong used by women, who
were paid three-halfpence an acre for spreading " clats "
(heaps of dung) about the fields. In one the two " grains "
are close and almost parallel, and it was fitted to the handle
by two iron " straps " which enclosed the wood. In another
the grains diverge more widely, and instead of straps it has
a single notched tail or " steart " which was driven into the
handle. As Henry Hazell says " steart," curling the " r "
round his tongue and giving the word two syllables, it
approximates most nearly to its original Anglo-Saxon, but it
is the same word that the Vicar unconsciously uses when in
April he tells the schoolchildren to watch for the coming of

A Wagon Middle-staff.

the redstart, and the same word again that shows on his tithe map as " Sterts," the narrow field between Ludbourne and the Wavering.

It is saddening to see such handsome things fallen on evil days, and encouraging by contrast is the sight of a middle-staff newly made for a bow-raved wagon. This is the iron buttress that supports the rave at mid-length, and at the same time, like the wooden strouter, strengthens the side of the wagon. At the base it is ornamented with a simple pattern—a cross with a spot in each of the four angles. The staff branches into two finely curving stays that are bolted into the rave, and where they part is a hook through which the ropes that tie down the load of hay or corn may be secured. The middlestaff is but one of the many irons for carts and wagons that the smith must make. Chains, bolts, hooks, bands, each with its special name, are required, not to speak of the tyres, the making and putting on of which is a highly specialised craft.

The village will lose far more than its wagons and its gates when these cease to be made, or cease to be made by hand ; far more than its smith and carpenter when they can no longer live by their trade ; how much it will lose would be hard to measure. Machinery has its right and useful functions. No one, for instance, who sees Daniel Jeffries' saw cutting its sure and effortless way through a gigantic elm trunk could without sentimentality wish for the days when this was the exhausting and monotonous work of the sawyer. Least of all would the sawyer himself regret the change. Yet even his work was far less monotonous than the daily occupation of the factory hand, and he himself was a far more intelligent workman. He had to train his eyes, his hands, his judgment, though to a lesser degree than had the wheelwright. The more skilled was the craft the more were the whole of the craftsman's faculties called into play. The worker in wood or in iron must learn what were the qualities and what the limitations of the material, and must use all his resource and invention in making the best use of both. His sight and his touch must respond instantly to soundness or inferiority in whatever he handled; he must hate to see a fine thing spoiled, and must persevere with infinite patience and self-criticism till what he was making was perfect as it could be made. His were good standards, and he knew that what served its purpose ill could never look well. There was no formula he could learn by rote, no rule of thumb that he could apply unintelligently to each task that came his way, for they differed as individuals differ, and as individuals he had to get to know them, respecting their idiosyncrasies, making allowances for them, humouring them, perhaps—getting the best out of them. It did not matter to him that he himself would not use what he was making: whether it were his or another's there was but one way of making it, and he made for the generations that came after him as well as for his own. There was no room for petty selfishness and jealousy in true craftsmanship; whoever found a new way or improved on an old one shared his discovery and it became part of the tradition followed by all the fellow-craftsmen who came after him. When each man saw the carrying through of a whole task from start to finish there was little cause for shelving responsibilities, for friction between master and man, for nice distinctions as to what was one man's job and what another's. The same good feeling obtained between trade and trade: smith helped wheelwright and wheelwright smith, and at a critical moment such as the tyring of a wheel, smith, smith's boy, wheelwright's apprentice and master wheelwright worked together as one man.

Small wonder that the generation of these craftsmen was more robust, both in character and in taste, than is the generation of machine workers who, without knowledge either of the conception of their work or of the end in view, can only repeat automatically one process of it until, tired out, they thirst for the relaxation of machine-made pleasures. True, they still have as their inheritance the art of their fathers, instinct with their personalities—the enduring things they made, their stone buildings and their tools of wood and iron. But those who no longer make soon lack the power to see, and then no-one is the richer for these riches, and none cares when they pass away.

Part Three

THE VILLAGE YEAR

Spring.—Rare flowers · Herb gathering ·
The woodman · Flowers of the hedges
and woods · Birds.

Summer.— Trees · Field   flowers · The
" stout " · Haymaking · Roadside flowers ·
Gardens.

Autumn.—Apples · Harvest Festival · Bonfire Night.

Winter.—Gipsies · The Village Shop and
Post Office · The Christmas Waits · Frost
and snow.

"ALL the ground on that side of the river was champain; fruteful of corne and grasse, but little wood." So wrote Leland. Aubrey called it "a soure, woodsere land." And Cobbett said of it, "This is a cheese country; some corn, but generally speaking it is a country of dairies. The ground is a stiff loam at top, and a yellowish stone under." All these descriptions are true. One need not go far beyond the confines of Kington Manor to find light brown cornbrash, full of small stones, yellow clay with grey clay under, dark rich loam, light red loam, dark sand, dark water-logged clay, and even spongy heath. There is accordingly a great variety of plant life, and not only variety, but plenty. The first primroses to appear—in White Stocking Lane they can always be found in January—are eagerly hunted and seized by children. A few weeks later, when they shine in every bank and hedgerow and fill all the copses, they are passed unheeded like weeds. So in early March there is a scramble for the best violet "marr" or plant; at the end of the month the flowers, the blue and the white, may lie strewn on the road as they fell from an idle hand. Primroses lose their brilliance and give place to bluebells and garlic; in the fields the gold of dandelions is succeeded by the gold of buttercups, then by the white and rust of moondaisies and sorrel; the hedgerows are lined with meadowsweet and willowherb instead of with cowparsley, and then the wayfaring tree ushers in the triumphal

White Helleborine.

procession of berries. All the time there is abundance: good measure, pressed down, filled to the brim and running over. There is a good share of the rarer flowers also. Small colonies of velvety bee orchises may be found on the tump at the branching of the Stanley Lane and in one of the thistly, hilly fields near the barrow. The butterfly orchis grows in Thickwood, and under a certain clump of beeches in July blooms white helleborine, the lovely waxy flower that looks as though it had grown in a hothouse. So many of the less common flowers are sinister looking— acrid stinking hellebore, its green petals dyed crimson at the rims; fleshy toothwort, the colour of a dirty white pig; broomrape, that is always old and brown; henbane, whose veins run blood; and herb paris, flower and no flower, with a black-bodied, green-legged spider at its heart.

Flowers that are as lovely as they are rare stand in more

peril. The meadows where snakeshead fritillary and summer snowflake grow and the wood of lilies-of-the-valley and Solomon's seal are now known to the motoring public. Other plants are vanishing for other reasons. A patch of henbane once grew by the Sutton roadside : now a cairn of blue granite marks its burial. The verges are cut every year just when the soapwort is coming into bloom, and not even its resemblance to garden phlox is a recommendation to

Snakeshead Fritillaries.

mercy at the hands of the roadman. The dyer's rocket, or weld, is being exterminated in the same way. This plant, which is like inordinately tall mignonette, is a reminder of the days of the flourishing wool trade, when a yellow dye was made from it. (Another link with those times is the teazle, which was used to raise the nap on the cloth. Teazles still abound here in the damper ditches, and are still used in the West of England cloth factories.) Meadow saffron has been, with difficulty, dug up from one of the fields where it grew because it poisoned the cattle. Wood betony, usually so common, almost disappeared one year from Lounces Leases, so greedily was it hunted by herb collectors. They, or rather the agents they supply, require also many other plants such as coltsfoot, ground ivy, yarrow, burdock and ragwort, all of which are so plentiful that there is enough and to spare. Less known herbs, such as the greater skull-cap, that grows in Herne Wood, are saved by the countryman's ignorance of his own flora. Seeing the bundles of herbs spread out to dry on the cottage roofs, the romantic would credit the villager with an old-time knowledge of herb-lore and a commendable industry in thus preparing his own remedies. The truth is that he neither knows nor cares to what purpose the plants are put, nor would he know their names were he not paid for the job. There are some of the older generation of whom this is not true. The smith, for instance, has always made concoctions of field agrimony as a tonic, and Mrs. Robbins at Priory Farm, who has a fine herb garden and dries her own parsley, mint, sage, marjoram and thyme for the kitchen, has great faith in tansy and camomile teas. On the whole, however, country folk recognise only the commoner flowers and the commoner birds. It is doubtful whether a schoolboy

Summer Snowflake.

would know a " scutty " from a " bluebottle " if he did not collect their eggs.

There are flowers that seem to bloom, in twos and threes if not all together, all the year round—dandelion, chickweed, red and white deadnettle, shepherd's purse, groundsel, plantain, black medick, hawkweed, thistle, and the little ivy-leaved toadflax that grows on walls. Some at least of these are to be seen, together with a few unexpected plants flowering out of season, even between October and March. From April onwards one can find from sixty to a hundred and twenty different flowers in a four-mile walk.

Winter aconite and stinking hellebore appear before any other plants are in bloom, and the only colour is the orange and crimson of willow and dogwood at the water's edge. In the wintry hedges the pale green of the hellebore flowers and the deep acid green of its bushy, long-fingered leaves are strikingly conspicuous, and the yellow aconite cups, resting

Henbane.

on their fringed ruffs, sometimes even peep above the January snow. Then come the hazel catkins. They prepare for the new year before they have shed their autumn leaves, and on the south side of Herne Wood they are flowering, loose as lambs' tails, as early as December. The little crimson tufts soon follow, when the rooks are repairing their nests in the reddening elms, the banks are beginning to put forth fresh leaves of honeysuckle, parsley, goosegrass, celandine and geranium, the spears of wild arum are thrusting through the leafmould, woodpeckers drum, and thrushes and blackbirds sing in the lengthening evenings, practising new phrases daily till their repertoire is full.

Henry Bird the woodman is still busy at this time of year in the glade of hazel " stowls " where the bushes have been cut. The branches of trees that fell during the winter gales must be fastened into the wooden cradle made for the purpose and then sawn up. The robin comes boldly near to eat the grubs that fall from the bark as the logs are thrown on to the heap. The wood is graded into pieces of Yule size and chumps for fuel, and of the hazel are made neat piles of small brushwood and bundles of sticking secured with thongs of their own branches. When the faggots are stacked round the trunks of the oaks they look like a small colony of primitive tents in a forest clearing. Henry Bird may not sell the wood, which is the property of Miss Everett, his employer, but he is allowed his own perquisites, and the close of every day sees him trudging home with a log on his shoulders. He usually puts another branch where his friend Stephen

Soapwort.

Tanner, who is a labourer at Allenford Farm, will find it on his way home to Stanley Fitzurse.

The opening of the first celandine marks the turning-point, and by the time these shining golden stars are changing to silver spring has come, with a rush of primroses, dog's mercury, wild strawberry, wood anemones and violets. Blue dog violets and sweet white violets are plentiful, but in these lanes the purple scented violet is rare. The sunshine lures out the brimstone butterflies ; the meadows on either side of Honeybrook are full of marsh marigolds and cuckoo flowers, with patches of purple-dyed bugle. All growth is thrusting upwards, drawn eagerly away from the earth towards the sun. In the hedgerow the erect spikes of white deadnettle point the way ; the smooth slender stems of Jack-in-the-hedge mount the bank almost visibly, showing daily more and more of their little white Easter crosses ; and behind them stream up goosegrass and starry stitchwort. Soon the Common is a Milky Way of daisies ; Kington people say that spring has come when you can tread on nine at once. In the forbidden copses plants as well as game live undisturbed. Here are found fragile woodsorrel and the small green dice of moschatel, and later, with the bluebells and garlic, feathery-leaved pignut, rose campion, herb paris, twayblade—commonest of the orchids—handsome wood spurge and wood sanicle, whose beauty lies in its inflorescence rather than in the flowers themselves. Golden archangel is as plentiful as white deadnettle. Near the edge of the wood grows sweet woodruff, smelling of new-mown hay—a dainty flower to bear the nickname of " woodreeve," the gamekeeper himself.

In March are celebrated the joint nuptials of all the frogs

in Cowlease pond. On the green surface of the water hundreds of tops of heads with protruding eyes are afloat, apparently disembodied, though in fact the submarine part of each frog is firmly anchored to his mate below. The first hot sunshine of the year finds a nest of young snakes coiling round one another.

It is only now and then that man stumbles by chance upon the secret life that is there all the year round if he has the will and the eyes and the patience to see—a glimpse of a

Meadow Saffron.

dog fox basking in the sun or pouncing on some small prey like a kitten ; of his vixen standing at bay with bared teeth, defying entry to the path leading to her cubs ; the unearthly noise of death-throes when he raids the poultry yard; the sound of his sharp bark at night. A sparrow hawk flies off with a thrush's egg, startlingly blue against the brown of the bare hedge, held in its beak; a flock of small birds mobs a marauding magpie. A pair of little owls make love, calling one to the other from an upper and a lower branch of a sapling elm. She flies off to a gatepost, he follows, and they mate. On a mossy stone beneath a clump of primroses perches a tiny wren, sipping from the stream. A rabbit, insane as a dog let off its leash, tears round and round a tree-trunk, then suddenly calms, and, sitting up on its hind legs, washes its face with its forepaws. At twilight an ancient badger comes from his earth and sharpens his claws on a beech bole; and a hedgehog hurries along, snuffling as he goes, then lifts up his voice and cries like a baby.

Now there is real warmth in the sun, and the chiff-chaff, that is always heard first in Five Thorns Lane from the twentieth of March to the end of the month, calls its name happily all day. The great tit sings two syllables like the chiff-chaff, but he stresses the first only, which makes his song sound half as monotonous and twice as vigorous. Cuckoos seldom arrive before the seventeenth of April—a date which often seems to mark the peak of the spring—but once they do come they are much in evidence, calling one to another or continuously, near and far, on the wing or from the trees, in every interval from a second to an augmented fourth. By May the hens are uttering their excitable, bubbling cries as they oar their way low over the fields. The air is noisy with birdsong, and no one in Kington Borel can sleep after half-past four, when the dawn chorus begins.

First, while owls are still hooting and cocks crowing, there is a subdued twitter, as though some bird were awake and feared to rouse the others. Faint and far off the cuckoo calls; it is thus he is heard when he first comes in April. Then a blackbird gives the alarm, and suddenly all the world is a charm of birds. The thrush sings jubilantly, each phrase twice, three times, four times; the blackbird chooses his favourite perch and pours out his rich contralto with the questioning inflections of human speech. There is a certain blackbird that always sits on a gable-end of the Almshouses. He is like a boy, cheekily whistling snatches of popular tunes:

Here and there some individual voice can be distinguished above the clamour. The corncrake's rasping note is heard almost continuously. Whitethroats, that have just arrived, gabble in the hedges; a green woodpecker laughs as he dips and scoops over the fields; the woodpigeon croons: " Tak' TWO COOS, tak' two." The willow warbler cries, "Weep, weep," and utters her little sentence with the dying fall. The

Stinking Hellebore.

chaffinch sings his brisk and rhythmical phrase; the wren asserts herself in a song surprisingly vigorous for so small a bird. Only a few sounds are discordant—the squawks of the jay and the pheasant and the predatory chatter of the magpie. The jay and the magpie are everybody's enemies; they are garden thieves and field thieves. It is they that rob the early nests of thrush and blackbird, who, while the branches are yet bare, build nests so obvious that they remind one of small children playing Hide the Thimble. Even easier to steal are the clutches of pheasants' eggs laid on the ground. That is why the shrivelled corpses of jays and magpies swing from the line near the gamekeeper's cottage, with the bodies of owls, stoats, weasels and squirrels—not all red squirrels either, for the wicked grey "tree rat" is now crossing the border into this county. Owls kill rats, stoats kill rabbits

Woodland Flowers. *Solomon's Seal, Herb Paris, Yellow Pimpernel, Moschatel, Lily-of-the-Valley, Wood Sorrel, Woodruff, Garlic and Spiked Star of Bethlehem.*

that overrun the village gardens. But this the gamekeeper must not consider; it is his duty to keep the pheasants so safe and so tame that the September guns cannot miss their mark.

Early in May one is aware of a new note in the morning choir—the croon of the turtle dove. There is one that has come three years running to a certain hedge in Lower Sams. She even comes to the same part of the hedge; perhaps she would even seek the same nest if she made nests that would outlast the weight of one full-grown pair of twins. The first year she came she was alone. Alone she built the crazy little house, strutting about with her mouthful of twigs so proudly; she laid her two eggs and sat on them, still purring contentedly, waiting for them to hatch; and then she abandoned them. Next year she returned with a mate, and together they built, a few yards from the spinster nest, and reared two scraggy and pugnacious youngsters, who would sit up on their precarious raft and peck if curious hands came too near. Soon the babies could not be distinguished from their parents, and by mid-August all four were gone. Next year the parents—or were they the children?—were back again, and again there were four turtledoves in Lower Sams.

There are other places beloved of certain birds. Year after year in the last week of April swifts begin to build under the tiles of the church. Martins choose Church Farm, and the first swallow is always seen skimming over Shepherd's Pond on April 8th or soon afterwards. The last week in May might be called Starling Week. These birds seem gregarious in hatching as in everything else, and at this time every roof in Kington Borel is busy with fussing parent birds, who in their indefatigable exertions for their hungry young make amends for their own greed throughout the rest of the year. Peewits, yellowhammers, meadow pipits and larks keep strictly to the upland fields and hedges. For several years in succession a pair of nightingales came to White Stocking Lane, but one winter the hedges were ruthlessly trimmed and the lane cleared. Perhaps the nightingales did not recognise the place the following spring; at any rate, they have not been there since, although in the oak woods beyond the stream they pour out their infinite variety of liquid notes as richly at midday as at midnight. All along the Wavering there are herons; perhaps Herne Wood takes its name from them. Coal tits haunt the larch plantation, and the dead fir by the path to Mount Pleasant is never without its spotted woodpecker. There are six or seven holes, the newest betrayed by the flecks of sawdust at the foot of the tree. Kingfishers nest under the little bridge near Bydemill, and the banks of the lane close by are often chosen by robins. Last year one nest contained not its rightful occupants, but an aggressive young cuckoo that opened its beak in an angry swear, showing the orange rubbery lining, if it thought its right of ownership was being challenged; the credulous robins slaved all day to supply its insatiable appetite. The ivied walls of the Vizzards' cottage have many nests every spring: chaffinch, robin, wren, and always thrush and blackbird. Unless one is watching these two birds at work it is not easy to tell until they are completed which nest is which, for the blackbird, too, makes a mud-lined nest; then she carries the building a stage further and gives it a soft inner layer. Sometimes birds mate before St. Valentine's Day, and if so they are nearly always doomed to disappointment. Frost and snow come, and the problem is how to feed the young and yet keep them warm. Early one February, when Mrs. Vizzard was laid up for a fortnight, a thrush built in the fork of a clothes prop that leaned against the wall, and laid four eggs. Three of them hatched; the fourth was addled. She would sit for hours at a stretch, the cruel east wind blowing the snow on to her back, trying to shelter the chicks. Footsteps, however near, never frightened her off, though the sudden click of the latch sometimes alarmed her. Meanwhile the young ones were becoming hungry, and she would at length fly off in search of food for them. It was not easy to find, for the starlings gobbled most of the crumbs Tiddle Vizzard put out every morning, and all the berries had vanished long ago. At the time when she needed most help there was apparently no mate to relieve her; perhaps the frost had killed him, as it did many other birds at the time. At last she, too, succumbed, or else gave up the struggle, and Mrs. Vizzard removed the deserted nest with the three little ugly, naked bodies, stone cold as the egg beside them.

That same year a robin had a nest on the window-sill. The bird showed a timidity unusual for one of her kind. On returning with a mouthful of titbits for her babies she would stand on tiptoe—or that is what it looked like—and peer through the window to make sure that no one was watching before she would venture to cram the food into the gaping throats. Kington birds have chosen some queer places. Twice a blue tit has brought off a brood in the wall letter-box at Mount Pleasant, and with all four thick hedges of Lounces Leases to choose from a certain blackbird elected to make her nest in the middle of the hayfield, where it was only dis-

HEDGE FLOWERS

covered when Obby 'Ancock frightened her off with his mowing machine. He mowed all round her while he debated what to do. Finally he removed the nest from its island of long grass to a hedge, but the blackbird did not fancy it there, and deserted.

Several birds less commonly seen in North Wiltshire appear quite at home in this village. The firs that top the barrow are the home of the tiny goldcrest. The lesser spotted woodpecker runs up the apple trees in the cottage gardens; the blackcap sings, only less sweetly than the nightingale, in Thickwood. Dipper and grey wagtail haunt the streams, and late in April the cock redstart comes house-hunting.

Spring seems no sooner here than it is gone, and first the blackthorn, then the cherry, then the crab, shed their petals. In richly wooded country such as this it is in the trees that the change of the season is most apparent. The first to burst its buds is the elder, but it seldom gets the credit for it : the olive of the young shoots is so much the colour of the branches. The chestnut is the first to be noticed—the buds are so fat and so sticky ; then the willow and the silver birch feather over with young leaves, sycamore buds swell and shed their rosy scales, and beneath the alders the bank of the Wavering is crimson with fallen catkins. The beech is a hardy tree, that will flourish on the windswept Downs as well as here in the shelter of Herne Wood, yet it is reluctant to unfurl its silken leaves fully till May is well launched and the Bramelham road is white with hawthorn. The oak is next, with young olive-coloured leaves and bunches of catkins. When the flowers are ripe the pattering of the black pollen grains to the ground below sounds like small rain. Last of all are the ash and walnut, which seem no sooner clothed than it is time to shed their leaves again.

The finest trees are in the hedgerows rather than the woods, where they are often too crowded to grow naturally. There is a magnificent line of elms in Pennycroft, planted in 1752. The fifteen cost twelve and sixpence, but three times that sum was expended altogether, in "posts for ffencing, for halling Trees, and to John Minty and Daniel Wilkins for Planting the Trees, one day and a half." Six years later four limes and six elms were planted in Tyne End. The limes and three of the elms are still standing, but the other three elms and two of those in Pennycroft have succumbed to the strange disease that attacks these trees from the top downwards. Since then very few trees have been set save a plantation of larches at the far end of Parson's Ground, and beautiful though they are when they are first coming into green and are putting forth their mulberry-coloured flowers, they are not trees of the south country, and are grown only to be felled. But the lime is handsome all the year through —when the bare tree is the shape of a skeleton leaf of its own, when the new growth of twig and bud turns redder and redder with the approach of spring, when the fresh young green appears, when the whole tree is a-hum with bees in the heavily-scented flowers, and when in early autumn the pale gold leaves flutter down. And it is the elms, because they are common as weeds, that show most surely the time of the year. Winter lasts so long as their bare shapes are outlined on the sky ; when the February sun strikes their flowering crests reddish purple against the dark raincloud spring has come, and soon the boles will be green with young leaves

Flowers of the Hayfield. *Grasses, Plantain, Knapweed, Hawkweed, Buttercup, Moondaisy, Spotted Orchis, Sheepsbit Scabious, Bugle, Clover, Yellow Rattle, and Germander Speedwell.*

and the ground scattered with seeds ; when they are heavy with masses of dark foliage it is high summer.

Now in the meadows the dandelions are all clocks, and cowslips and early purple orchises give place to the flowers of the hayfield—clover, sorrel, moondaisies, ragged robin, hawkweed, wood betony, quaking grass—" wagwants," the children call them—" tinker tailors " and other grasses, lucerne and vetches, the pyramidal orchis, and the spotted orchis like a faded lilac print frock, and yellow rattle, which should have no place in a hayfield but always contrives to be there.

Summer brings but one thoroughly unwelcome visitor to these rich meadows—the " stout," as Kington people call the gadfly. He comes with the ripening of the haygrass, and he chooses certain prey only—the florid and full-blooded. Pharaoh's lean kine are not for him. Some warm, damp day the victim is aware of a sound he has not heard since early September—a soft buzz, unlike that of any other fly. Then he sees the creature—its dirty grey-brown body, its large head, its wings a-blur like a spinning-top, waiting to pitch on his back and thence to creep to the juiciest part of hand or neck and stab deep—whatever its origin, the word " stout " shows a sense of onomatopoeia common in country nomenclature. There it stays, so sickeningly engrossed in its feast of blood that it does not see the hand uplifted to strike, or, if it sees it, would sooner die drinking than live unsatisfied. So it dies, leaving as legacy so fierce a swelling that the memory of it sometimes lingers in the flesh a whole summer through.

Haymaking begins early in June ; then if rain should follow there may be an aftermath. Every minute of daylight is used, from dawn of the first day, when the mower knives cut crisply through the dew-drenched grass, till dusk of the last, when neighbours as well as farmhands join in the work of hoisting the haycocks on their pitchforks to the men making the ricks. The mighty octogenarian wagon lumbers towards the field. " She ' boxes ' well," says Simeon Robbins proudly : he can recognise a mile away the sound that tells him that she is well set on her wheels. By the time the field is clean as a lawn darkness is falling and the moon has risen, and from the farm the movement of the wagon along the lane can be discerned only by the sound and by the white smocks of the men leading the two horses.

Haysel over, there seems a sudden dearth of colour. But

Water Avens.

if the meadows look empty and shorn, and the only stretches of brightness are where poppy and charlock grow or rosebay willowherb clothes the newly-made clearings of the larch plantation, more varieties of flowers than ever are to be found. Although the woods have passed their prime some of the flowers of May are still blooming—water avens, peach-coloured within, wine-red without ; yellow pimpernel, dangling its twin stars on slender stalks ; creeping Jenny, that fills all the ground space with a pattern of leaves and flowers ; enchanter's nightshade, whose name is more romantic than its appearance ; and the tall spiked Star of Bethlehem, which is not recognised here as an asparagus, and so is left to flourish. The hedges are at their loveliest, with the wild roses that come with the first of June, and the fragrant cream meadow roses that grow lower in the hedge. The air is heavy with the scent of elder and privet, and buckthorn and guelder rose are in bloom. Wayfaring tree is already beginning to form green berries, and blackberry and dewberry blossom and the flowers of white and of black bryony give promise of autumn.

Now, too, is the time when the wilderness blossoms as the rose. The waste strips by the white upland roads are set close with a thousand flowers of many colours : the purple of thistles and knapweed, the misty blue of harebell and sheep's bit scabious, the yellow of bird's foot trefoil, silver-weed, bedstraw, rock rose and tormentil. Here within arm's reach are field gentian, meadow vetchling, yellow-wort, pink-starred centaury, rest harrow, little eyebright and thyme, greeny-yellow parsnip, gromwell, horehound and wild basil, and there in the coarser grass handsome fleabane and blue chicory that has escaped from the cornfield close by. There

Houndstongue.

are flowers so inconspicuous that they are seen only if searched for—knotgrass, field madder, bartsia, and tiny white cathartic flax. Others show, in this short turf, more brightly than their size might warrant. Field bindweed—withwind, as it is called here—grows in the road itself; while blue and white milkwort, strawberry clover, scarlet pimpernel—the "poor man's weather-glass"—and dove's foot cranesbill creep as near as they dare. This is cranesbill time. Herb Robert and wild geranium are still in their prime; the round-leaved and jagged-leaved varieties flower here and there; the pretty, feathery-leaved musk stork's bill on the wall is showing its pointed beaks, and meadow cranesbill, most showy of all the summer flowers, is coming into bloom. The old quarry at Mount Pleasant is by no means given up to docks and nettles; there are bright patches of poppy mingled with camomile and bladder campion, and smaller sprinklings of fumitory, melilot, wild mignonette, and, more rare than the others and more strange, houndstongue, the plant with the strong animal stench, downy grey leaves, and flowers of the richest, darkest, most glowing red. No other wild flower approaches this colour unless it be the figwort, which is now beginning to bloom at the water's edge, beside the tousled hemp agrimony, or in ditches, rising from damper levels of brooklime and water speedwell and forget-me-not, past white and purple comfrey and meadowsweet, to join the tall rank growth of hemlock, angelica and "codlins and cream."

Deadly Nightshade.

Now cottage gardens are at their gayest. Bramelham Long Fair, which is held on August Bank Holiday, awards a prize for the best kept, and there is keen rivalry. Certain competitors even plan their sowing with this date alone in view: from October till April there is nothing to be seen but bare earth; from April to early July nothing but regularly-spaced spots of green; then there is a gradual dawning of the splendour that will reach its height in the first week in August. But the average cottager prefers some bloom in his garden all the year round. He likes to see the same flowers year after year in their wonted places, and but seldom succumbs to the suggestion in wireless talk or gardening magazine to try some new variety. Yellow wallflowers he plants always near the house, red farther off; thrift, catmint, pinks or saxifrage bordering his paths, stocks below the windows when the " polyanthums " are over, tulips to rise stiffly from between rows of fading crocuses. But if he is unimaginative where arrangement is concerned, he has a child-like love of bright colour, and Nature so has it that whether he " shows " at Bramelham Long Fair or not, at this time of the year his plot will most satisfy him. There are sweet peas, climbing on their rather too professional scaffolding; roses and clematis and honeysuckle and hollyhocks that vindicate even the most sentimental of pictures; bushes of lavender, overblown because they have already yielded enough and to spare for the linen cupboards, white alyssum to set off the many rich reds and golds—for gardens seem, like trees, to flame in a final brilliance before they wither into winter, and now they are afire with red-hot pokers, dahlias and oriental poppies, with crimson snapdragons and orange nasturtiums and marigolds.

August has its special wild flowers also. This is the time to look for deadly nightshade in the thicket near Priory Farm, for water lilies on Bydemill pond, and for viper's bugloss on the Stanley Lane tump where in June bee orchises grew. Beside Honeybrook is yellow loosestrife growing with the purple, and Sunday Mead has a fine patch of the rare greater spearwort, that looks at a distance like buttercups blooming out of season. The mellow heat draws out the aromatic scent of thyme and marjoram and ploughman's spikenard in the sunny lanes and of watermint in the fields, where the meadow brown butterflies flutter like leaves.

There is little wind, and the birds are silent except for certain voices that went unnoticed while the cuckoo still

Greater Spearwort.

clamoured—the monotonous note of the greenfinch, that sounds as though it were made with sucking lips ; the rich musical gabble of the garden warbler, the twitter of linnets, and the yellowhammer's " little-bit-of-bread-and-NO-cheeeese." The bullfinch flits about with his grown-up family, the spotted flycatcher turns somersaults in the air, the tree-creeper runs up the oak like a little mouse and is lost to sight in the thick foliage. As sunset changes to dusk the scream of the swift ceases, and the white owl flutters silently, like a moth, below the cottage eaves.

130

This is the busiest time of the year for the farmer. The transition from haysel to harvest is imperceptible—Priory Farm is often reaping its first oats before Berry Farm has carted its last hay. Apple harvest, too, has begun. First to ripen are the Beauties of Bath. Mrs. Comely has a fine tree, and since they will not keep, she gives many away to the children, who like their tart flavour and their bright skins, mottled with pink that soaks through to the core. Next come Mrs. Jeffries' large rosy Worcester Pearmains, which she sells in the market, and then, one after another, all the other kinds, most of them nameless, because no-one knows what kindly cottager planted these trees for other generations to enjoy. There are Mrs. Tucker's long, rather "sleepy" yellow apples, old Mrs. Webb's huge dumpling apples, Bob Wilkins' pumpkin-shaped ones, coloured like the fruit that the wicked stepmother offered Snow-white—one side bright red, the other bright green.

These are apples that look their best at the time of the Harvest Festival. Every September there are piles of them at the foot of the great Norman pillars of the chancel arch, for long custom has by now decreed whose offering shall lie where on this solemn occasion. The sheaves of wheat that make obeisance at the communion rail are from Priory Farm; the oats and barley in the nave are Caleb Drewett's; Joe Gingell makes the small ricks that stand on the altar, and George Knapp at the White Hart the cottage loaves. Mrs. Eeles, from the Flemish Houses, selects her largest and brownest eggs and puts them in the special basket—made by Abel Wootton—that she keeps for the purpose. These, too, have a place of honour on the altar table, and to match them the other side are Daniel Jeffries' Cox's Orange Pippins in their basket. It is a pity that the Freeths attend chapel, for the dahlias at Maslin Farm are the best in Kington Borel, but the single ones in Mrs. Sealy's country bunch look very well, with Michaelmas daisies and giant sunflowers. Mrs. Sealy likes her flowers to be in the south window, where she can look at them during the service. Obby 'Ancock would like his enormous marrow to be there too—he sits just behind the Sealys—but it is too big, so it stands near the door, where the legend cut in its rind is the first thing seen by those coming in—" Praise ye the Lord. A.H. 19——". The great sack of potatoes opposite, the pick of the Manor's kitchen garden, is the only thing large enough to balance it, for, like other Kington gardeners, Albert does not believe a vegetable should be eaten till it has reached its maximum size. The window embrasures are piled high with well-scrubbed carrots, turnips and parsnips, and with cabbages like huge green roses, and the air is heavy with a rich earthy smell— half greengrocer's shop, half barn. On the Monday following the festival the produce is sent to the nearest hospital, though Mrs. Beak, who happened to be there with a broken leg one September, declared, " Us never got none on it."

The storage of apples is always something of a problem. Worthy Vines used to insist on keeping his Bramleys under the bed, to the annoyance of his daughter Thirza, who had to move them every time she swept. Mrs. Cole spread hers in the roof, but the mice soon smelt them and, climbing up by way of the wash-house roof, found an entry between the tiles. One day, on looking through her dormer window, Mrs. Cole saw close to the sill a long, lithe, brown body that vanished like lightning when she turned the hasp. It dawned upon her what the weasel was looking for ; she lit a candle, climbed the rung ladder against the wall, and opened the trap-door. Sure enough, the apples had been nibbled, and there was a half-finished nest, made of the sacking on which they were laid. Mice have many enemies—the steel trap, the hovering hawk, the silent owl, the cruel cat, the grass snake, that slobbers her victim with saliva and mauls him till he is of a shape convenient to be swallowed.

Now comes a succession of those days that begin with mist and gossamer, open into a splendour of blue and gold, and end with the rise of the harvest or of the hunter's moon. The robin utters his sweet minor phrases as he waits upon the spade that is preparing garden beds for the spring. There is so much fruit in the hedges that even after all the elderberry wine, " slawn " (sloe) gin, and blackberry jelly and vinegar have been made, much is left to drop from the bushes. There are still plenty of nuts for the squirrel—for the children were more interested in the earlier than in the later, riper crops. Beneath the oaks in the farm pastures the ground is churned up by the snouts of pigs foraging for acorns. Boys throw stones at the chestnuts to bring down even larger and more burnished " conkers " than are lying under the tree. The hedges are loaded as for a Bacchanal with the purple of dogwood and the gold of maple, wreaths of succulent bryony berries and withered hops and clouds of old man's beard. There is one colour brightest even amid this brilliance—the rare pink of the spindle berries, parting to show their orange seeds. The wealth of crimson " Peggy ailes "—or haws— polished black privet berries and scarlet hips causes the villagers to prophesy annually a " main 'ard winter." With the first white frost the leaves begin to turn—first ash, then

Spindle Berries.

lime, then chestnut and poplar, then the elm in yellow patches ; then the beech flames into auburn, the oaks ripen, and the spotted sycamore shrivels away. The fall of the leaf seldom happens here before November ; if the autumn gales are late the trees are still clothed at the end of the month.

With the stormy winds flocks of gulls come inland, conspicuous on the newly-ploughed fields. Then, just as the sight of a line of martins on the telegraph wires is a reminder that the swifts have already gone, with none to note the day of their departure, one is aware some October day of a gleam of red in the thrushes—these are no song-thrushes, but redwings from Scandinavia. Now the " chack-chack-chack " of the fieldfares is heard—another sign of approaching winter.

There is much to be done in farm and garden before the cold weather sets in. The stubble must be ploughed and winter wheat sown, and there are swedes and mangolds to be lifted and stored in long mounds covered with turf or thatch. The empty potato patch is roughly dug so that the frost may do its work there ; fruit trees are pruned and grass plots are cut for the last time ; wallflowers are primly set in the beds where aster and marigold have flowered, and everywhere rises the blue fragrant smoke of bonfires.

It may be the necessity for some such annual clearance rather than any special significance in the event it commemorates that has caused the ritual of Guy Fawkes' Day to be perpetuated. For the children of Kington Borel the mighty bonfire on the common on November the Fifth is the greatest event of the year.

As soon as school re-opens after the summer holidays they begin to forage for wood, brambles, garden refuse— anything that will burn—and stack it on Upper Common, not far from the pound. Formerly there were three bonfires in competition : one near the signpost in Barbarans Lane, one at Frogwell, and the third here ; but the Frogwell fire would go out every time, and Emmy Tucker, who lives near the signpost, became increasingly nervous lest the sparks from the Barbarans Lane bonfire should light on her thatch. So it was decided that there should be one bonfire only ; it could be as big as the three put together—and it is. As November the Fifth draws nearer and its height still fails to satisfy, the children go out with their home-made trucks by moonlight to see what they can find. The finishing touches are made on November the fourth by Henry Hazell, the smith, who, since he is the prince of stokers, has been appointed by common consent master of the ceremonies.

For the children the festivities begin immediately after tea. Grown-ups are not encouraged to attend this part of the ceremony—the setting off of fireworks bought at Mrs. Comely's. This fun is of necessity short-lived, since the resolution to save all the fireworks for the Fifth invariably proves too hard to keep. At last comes the magic moment when Henry Hazell, having washed and had his tea, is ready to light the bonfire. The tin of paraffin and the carefully-placed paper do their work; the brambles crackle, up shoot the flames, and even the bolder spirits fall back a pace or two. The pungent reek of the smoke is wafted as far as Bramelham Gate. All the familiar surroundings become visible again in the red glare—the walls of the pound, the gables of the Flemish buildings, the well-house, Stocks Tree. Now the fire flickers lower—it must have found the layer of wet goldenrod from the Vines's garden. Henry comes to the rescue. A sudden flare shows his silhouette, prodding the thorns with his hayfork; he looks like a devil in some old picture of Hell. How rosy in this light are the rosy faces; how red the red mufflers; how black the darkness behind the charmed circle ! But even this bonfire cannot last for ever, and eventually it becomes apparent that its prime is past. The children tire of playing at ordeal by fire, and the mothers call them home, leaving the fathers still enjoying themselves.

Kington Borel abounds with holly bushes and with mistletoe, which likes the hawthorn trees. It is wise to pick early for Christmas, for the fame of these berries travels far at this season. The worst holly-pilferers are the gipsies. They load their carts by night, and in the day come coolly hawking their wares to the very people they have robbed. The nomadic gipsy is, to say the least of it, not beloved by the village householder. Once a small company encamped in Five Thorns Lane. They begged from the nearest cottager, Sarah Minty, first water—that seemed a reasonable request—then bread, which was less easy to spare, then stockings, which she refused. Then came the wheedling question, " I suppose you haven't a tail ? " And Sarah, who could not afford to give away a skirt even if she had realised that that was what the woman wanted, shut the door in her face. That night a thick hoar frost settled on the roof of the caravan, and the gipsies sat round the large fire they had made—melodramatic-looking men, sulky women with plaits and earrings, some dozen black-eyed children—all as beautiful as animals and as lacking in morals. The next morning the women and older children went off to town with their baskets, and the men stayed behind and made clothes pegs from the sticks they had cut from the hedges. But news of their presence had filtered through to the policeman at Sutton Pinkney (for Kington Borel has none of its own) and before the women had returned he arrived and moved the encampment on. The ponies were caught—they could not wander far because of the chains on their feet—the caravans were harnessed, the fire was stamped out, the pegs and the babies were collected with a rapidity born of frequent practice, and the little procession filed out of the village; pathetic, not consciously, but with the pathos of the unwanted. They left much litter—straw they had used for bedding the horses, pieces of whittled sticks and tin filings, dirty rags, rubber tyres for firelighters, feathers (from whose hen?) and crusts of bread. The lane did not regain its respectability till Charlie Cole came to do the hedging and ditching.

The scarcity of berried holly in the hedges is one of the many signs of the near approach of Christmas. There are more fat geese and turkeys going to Bramelham market; the bus is fuller on Fridays, and the spicy smell of boiling puddings is wafted from the housewives' coppers. There are larger crowds than usual round the butcher's van that calls at Kington Borel on Saturday afternoon. Mrs. Coates wants her middle cut of brisket of beef, to be rubbed with black treacle, spices and saltpetre every day till Christmas Eve, when she will boil it with the hock in readiness for the visit of her son and his family. Mrs. Gingell has ordered pig's cheek to make into brawn, and there is a general demand for suet. Dusk has fallen before the van has finished its round, and it is illuminated cosily from within. The light falls on the upturned faces of some dozen children and dogs clustered expectantly at the open double doors: they are waiting for the women to finish haggling over the price of backbone, cuttings or shin. At last it is their turn. The butcher doles them out—children and dogs alike—a large lump of suet apiece. "Does 'em good," he says. "Keeps 'em warm." Too pleased for thanks, the children run off, sucking their suet as they would a cornet ice, and the van moves on to Stanley Fitzurse.

Christmas is a busy time for Annie Comely, and the shop is more crowded than ever. Pink Christmas stockings dangle from a coloured paper-chain stretched across the already low ceiling; the inkpot gets mislaid behind the raisins, and there is only just room among the brown paper parcels and the home-made plum cakes on the counter for the tray of Christmas cards, gay with unseasonable roses and pansies and shiny with embossed celluloid. Sometimes the post office till runs out of small silver, and some must be borrowed from the caramel tin containing the shop takings—a procedure frequently entailing much mental arithmetic, in which the co-operation of all the waiting customers is sought. But nothing seems to disturb Mrs. Comely's equanimity. She has been postmistress ever since the death of her mother eighteen years ago, and even when Mrs. Archard was alive Annie helped whenever she was home ; it was she, in fact, who had bought the letter-box for her mother with her first savings in service : she had paid two pounds to have it set in the wall beside the shop window. There were fewer letters to cope with in those days, but the work was harder, for there was no red mail van, and the Archard household had to be sorters and postmen combined. John Beszant used to bring the letters from Bramelham at half-past six every morning, and Mrs. Archard would give him a big breakfast before he went on to Tiddley Winks. In the evening he had to do the walk again, sounding his horn at Bramelham Gate, at the signpost and again at the market cross to announce that he was collecting the mail. The Archards were saved two long tramps : Ted Clapp, who was a labourer at Allenford, would always deliver any letters for the farm there, and Milly Romaine, who was in service with the Freeths, took those for Maslin Farm. But the daily round was quite long enough for Dolly Archard, Annie's younger sister—first up Church Lane to Frogwell, then along Sawmills Lane to the Manor, because Squire liked his post early (for his letters there was a special locked bag that Dolly carried on her back), then across Cookrow to Lypgate. This often marked the limit of Dolly's walk westwards, unless there was to be a foxhunt, in which case there were postcards bearing the message, "Stop your earths to-day," which must go to Cold Harbour and Berry Farm. Her eastward journey was across the common, past the Market Cross to Bramelham Gate, then home along Five Thorns Lane and Silver Street. She can tell you now of one memorable occasion when, as she was going past the copse at the end of Waddling Street, she stopped, as was her wont (for she had a keen sense of fair play), to draw out the branches that blocked the entrances to the fox-earths there. She looked round to make sure that she was not being watched, and to her dismay saw one of the farm horses galloping straight for her. He had strayed into the lane and, not being able to find the way out again, was becoming excited. She screamed and made for the fence, but stumbled and fell in the mud, " scagging " her frock and dropping all the letters. The fall frightened the horse as much as it did her ; he turned suddenly round and bolted, while she picked herself up and with shaking hands tried to clean the dirty envelopes ; then she ran sobbing all the way back.

To-day the van takes letters along the chief roads and Mrs. Comely delivers those for the centre of the village while her husband minds the shop ; but at Christmas, when the head office at Bramelham needs all the extra help it can get, the village returns to the old way, and the younger Comely children go the long round that used to be their aunt's daily walk.

One old custom that is still kept up here is the singing of

HARVEST FESTIVAL

the waits on Christmas Eve. They are Tom Coates the
sexton and Teacher Miles, who sing bass, Bob Wilkins the
mason and Jim Gosling the undertaker, who are tenors, and
Daniel Jeffries for the alto parts. Anyone else who accom-
panies them comes in useful for the verses sung in unison.
They sing at three places in the village : at the wellhouse, by
the Market Cross, and outside the Manor. When Tom
Coates' father was sexton they used to start at midnight, and
when they had reached the Manor and had sung " While
shepherds watched," " Hark the herald angels sing," and
" God rest ye merry, gentlemen," and lastly " Good Christian men, rejoice," because that was the old Squire's favourite, he would ask them in and treat them all to mulled ale
and mince pies. But Miss Everett does not keep such late
hours as her uncle did, and so the waits begin their round
earlier. Otherwise the procedure is much the same as it
always was.

Though Christmas is more often green than white,
winter is not yet over. Sometimes there is hoar frost, when
trees are transformed to coral and cobwebs to lace, sometimes snow that is blown and then frozen into sweeping
white wings extending from the hedges. Severe weather is
far more common after Christmas than before, and seldom
does a year pass without a spell of hard frost when the fields
are bleached and the ground baked. Moorhens and nut-
hatches come close to cottage doors in search of food,
necessity banishing for the time being their fear of man. In
the dark weeks when both earth and water are sealed over,
the starling may be seen tunnelling with his beak in the snow
for a drink ; woodpigeons descend ravenously on the spring

cabbages and eat them bare, and the red squirrel, driven by sharp hunger from his hiding-place, gnaws at frozen twigs.

Life is harder even for human beings. The icy east wind blows under cottage doors, where footsteps have worn a hollow in the threshold. Milk freezes in the pail, and neighbours take it in turns to thaw the pumps. But for the children this is all part of the fun. Shepherd's Pond is " bearing," and they make a slide right across it, following one another shrieking in a long chain. The young men go by moonlight when work is done to the lake in Stanley Park, and play " hockey " with inverted walking-sticks. Most of them have skates, for although they are not on sale in the Bramelham shops there is usually a pair in the family, acquired so long ago that no one quite knows whose it is. It may be the old-fashioned wooden kind that screws into the heel of the boot ; its leather straps may have perished so that it has to be tied on with string ; it is probably the wrong size for the present wearer ; but there is no time to be fastidious when every available hour is precious right up to the day when the ice creaks ominously and there is an inch of water on the surface. For frosts, the older people say, are not as hard as they were ; why, when Emmy Tucker's mother was courting, her young man used to skate all the way from Swindon along the canal to see her.

There is no denying the picturesqueness of " seasonable " weather. The sun touches the crests of the snow with rose and gold, leaving the hollows violet ; the full moon shows the whole landscape uncannily clear, even to the cold white Downs. Now as at no other time the essential shapes of the trees are seen—the neat low hump of the oak, the graceful fans of the elm. Near at hand trunks and branches are bright

mossy green where the low afternoon rays strike them ; in
the distance they are inky blue against the white squares of
fields. But this country, wrapped in the sinister silence of
frost or seared with bitter winds, is not the beloved familiar
scene ; alien are the withered grasses rustling like paper, the
sky leaden with snow, the ponds in their mask of steely grey.
The whole land seems under an interdict. Then suddenly
comes the blessed thaw : the air blows soft from the west,
the earth yields to the tread, and the first lambs bleat in
the fields.

Part Four

VILLAGE PEOPLE

Common Surnames · Illegitimacy · Wooseting · Tombstones · Traces of the Woollen Industry · Old village surnames · Jack-of-all-trades · Weather-lore and superstitions · Vermin · Beginning of Fox-hunting · Cock-squailing · The local preacher · Smocks · The dressmaker · The midwife · A ghost story · The Doctor · The Vicar · Children's games · Local Dialect · Tales of the old Squire · Village philosophy.

WHEN one is in doubt as to a villager's name the chances are exactly one in ten that he is a Hancock —nine out of the ninety homes are inhabited by families of that name. There was much to be said for the old system of having letters delivered by the post-mistress. A postman newly sent from town soon finds himself in difficulties when the four hundred inhabitants have but fifty surnames between them. Very few of the cottages have names, and none has a number, though the arbitrary system of numbering has already invaded Stanley Fitzurse, with ludicrous results when, for instance, house number twenty is half a mile from number nineteen and happens to be much nearer to number four over the hedge. So it is left to the postman's discretion to distinguish the Garlicks beyond Frogwell from those near Bramelham Gate, or John Beak's family from Daniel Beak's, both on Lower Common. Mrs. Comely used to tell by the handwriting which letter was for which.

Most of the families of the same name are related. Village romances are still common, and were more so before buses, bicycles, lure of the town and unemployment took the young folk farther afield in their search for mates. You will be told that Obby 'Ancock's wife was " not a Kington girl," and may imagine that she hailed from London, or at least from Somerset. Not so : she was born and bred in Sutton Pink-ney, the next village, and her maiden name was Fry.

There was much intermarriage, yet there is only one village idiot, Tiddle Vizzard, and her insanity has another explanation. She is simple rather than silly, and though " sinful ornary " to look at, she is of so sweet and unaffected a nature that she is a general favourite, especially with the children ; yet, with the cruelty of their kind, they often torment her. The tale goes that a bat flew into the kitchen and out again on the night Joshua Vizzard was drowned, and so frightened his wife that Tiddle was born with webbed feet. A curious habit the girl has of creeping into corners and flapping her hands lends colour to the superstition that she resembles a bat, and the children will call out to her, " Tiddle-Tiddle Flittermouse, fly up in the air ! " half expecting her to do so. In happier hours she is found sitting on the common playing contentedly with daisy-chains or tisty-tosties (cowslip balls) among the cluster of infants, who understand her when grown-ups fail.

In some cases the frequency of a certain name has another explanation—illegitimacy in an earlier generation, the children having taken their mothers' names. " Getting into trouble " was formerly regarded as a misfortune rather than as a disgrace. It would have been hypocrisy on the part of the village matrons to affect disgust, since a large number of them had " had to get married." Such marriages were usually happy ; the circumstances had merely precipitated, not forced, the wedding. The further back in village history the commoner bastards seem to have been ; " baseborn " is entered against many a name in the parish register.

There was one misdemeanour, however, that the code of morality would not tolerate. It was adultery in which a married person with a family was concerned. The village showed its disapproval in no uncertain manner by a " woo-seting." The guilty pair were serenaded with a loud beating and rattling of pots and pans. If they could not be caught together, the victim was whichever of them was judged the guiltier. The ceremony that followed savoured more of tribal witchcraft than of Christian England : the effigies of the two delinquents, that had been carried round in the procession, were solemnly burned. The last occasion when a wooseting took place was but twenty-four years ago, when Mrs. Roberts, the widow of the gardener at Weavers' House, supplanted Lucy Webb in her husband's affections. The bonfire was made in Cowlease Ground at the back of Mrs. Roberts' cottage. She left the village soon afterwards to try her wiles elsewhere, and Samuel Webb shamefacedly returned to his former love.

There is village stock that goes back nine hundred years. Kington Borel has humble aristocrats whose names are recorded as Wiltshire tenants under the Conqueror ; though Caleb Drewett, William Ody and Jim Gosling might find it hard to believe that Drogo, Odo and Gozelin were their ancestors. Ernie Keynes does not know that he might boast of Norman blood through his descent from the Walter de Cahaignes who signed the deed when Johan Gengel's property changed hands. There is nothing to prove his ancestry save that country folk did not move far in eight hundred years, and if John of Kington or Thomas of Wiltshire was so venturesome as to leave his village or his county, he left only to return in course of time as John Kington or Thomas Wiltshire, his surname testifying to his wanderlust and his address to his homing instinct. Wilt-

shire is full of Wiltshires, and fifty years ago there were
Kingtons in Kington Borel. Abel Wootton, Benjamin
Brinkworth, Sarah Minty, Tom Coates and Job Notton all
bear the names of neighbouring villages.

Nor has character changed greatly with the passing of
years. It may be because the friendly familiarity of the villager persists through the centuries that names such as
Hawkins, Hancock and Robbins sound so appropriate.
Harry's, Jack's, or Bob's boy they would be called to-day ;
the formality of full baptismal names and titles is and always
has been dispensed with except on solemn occasions.
" Mother " Cole, " Widow " Russ, " Granfer " Blake, were
courtesy designations for old people, and the others needed
none. To-day, although married women keep their " Mrs."
in friendly conversation, their husbands invariably greet one
another by their Christian names—or nicknames, for a sense
of pattern has prompted them to make some adaptations. So
Henry Hazell is Henny, Albert Hancock is Obby (and then
the H of Hancock must go to match it), and Humphrey
Couzens is always Coffy ; nobody knows why. Worthy
Vines was so christened at the font, and, unbelievable though
his name sounds, it can be surpassed by many on the tombstones. There is a fine headstone to Swaine Harbin (whose
name yet lives in Harbin's Bottom, one of the fields he owned
at Allenford) bearing simply his name and " 1760," the date
of his death, surmounted by a carved cherub. And next to
it is a smaller stone inscribed in fine italics : " Here lyeth ye
Bodye of Charity ye wyf of Robt. Sweetaple." A second
stone marks the foot of the grave. While they yet lived,
Charity and Robert must have lain down at night in their
handsome family bed not unlike in shape and carving to

Tombstones.

these slabs. Not far away lies Pitaronell Merryweather beneath the massive weight of her square tomb that bears also the names of other Merryweathers—they were a " main long family "—each on its oval plaque. Among the tombs, some tilted out of the perpendicular with the passing of years, some spotted with orange lichen and crusted with moss, there are two on which the names of Habakkuk Heaven and Abimoloch Doggrell are still deciperable, while another com- memorates a certain Timothy Turtle. Timothy's ancestry was nobler than the simple headstone suggests. Thurcytel, a Norseman by descent, held Wiltshire lands from the Con- queror, and appears in Domesday Book as Torchitil, in company with names no less romantic—Nigel the physician, Gunfrid Maldoith, Waleran the huntsman, and Leviet, embroideress to the King and Queen.

It would be surprising if the weaving industry, that flourished here for three centuries, had left no mark on local names. The forbears of the Webbs and the Websters and the numerous Tuckers, as their names imply, were engaged in the wool trade, and the first Hawkinses and Wilkinses and other -kinses to be so called lived at a time when the language of the Flemish weavers who had settled among them was influencing English speech, surnames included. In the seventeenth century a Blanchard of Sutton Pinkney was bound apprentice to a weaver in Bramelham ; and the name of a contemporary of his, a certain John Gingell of Kington, appears in the Minute Book of the Company of Weavers of London. No doubt this was the ancestor of Joseph Gingell the thatcher, and a descendant of the Johan Gengell who " by reason of his poverty " surrendered his poor half-acre to the Abbot of Glastonbury.

Were Sir John Pierce of the Priory and Thomas Maskelyne at Mount Pleasant among the richly-dressed gentry whose wearing of " owe Traygous great Hosen " called for the sumptuary law in the reign of Queen Elizabeth, which said that garments should be only " of stuffe made and wroughte within her hyghnes Domyons ? " If so, it is more than likely that they thought the game worth the candle and continued in their vanity. At least, it was so with the Everetts two centuries later, when similar laws designed for the protection of the country's woollen industry were in force. They decreed that no corpse was to be " put in, wrapt, or wound up or Buried, in any Shirt, Shift, Sheet, or Shroud, made or mingled with Flax, Hemp, Silk, Hair, Gold or Silver or other than what is made of Sheeps wool only." The fine of fifty shillings a time made little impression on

Humphrey Everett, Gentleman, who continued to bury his dead in the customary linen, having his name entered in the parish register for his offence and the fine distributed to the poor. At last he himself was buried in linen by his heir, who was spared further fines by the repeal of the law.

There is scarcely a surname that cannot be traced in the annals of one or other of the surrounding villages. Sutton Pinkney churchyard is full of Comelys and Coles, and at Stanley Fitzurse generations of Bubbs, Freegards and Knapps are buried. And somewhere below those grassy mounds may lie the Tanner who carried his skins packsaddle to the shoemaker's, the Garlick who sold his savoury wares, the Vizzard with his strange headgear; and did their ghosts but walk one might see why that Sealy had been nicknamed for his innocence, and whether the first Blanchard was fair and the first Romaine swarthy, as their descendants are to this day.

Occasionally an entry in the parish accounts gives proof that the more startling events of history had their repercussions even in this small village. In 1557 a Giles Romaine of Kingtone was paid two shillings and fourpence for defacing the rood-loft at Sutton Pinkney church. Among those who contributed towards the expenses incurred in the defeat of the Spanish Armada was an Everett; and a Freegard was assessed for payment of ship money in Charles the First's reign. On the accession of Cromwell a William Hull was bidden to remove the royal arms from a Bramelham inn; eleven years later it was his job to set them up again!

Long local ancestry has left its hallmark on village

character. It is not by chance that among those bearing the names that have survived through the centuries in this particular part of the country are the most robust personalities of Kington Borel. Take Humphrey Couzens—" Coffy," as he is always called. As far back as the time of Henry the Second a Couzens owned a field on the outskirts of Bramelham. A Couzens was baptized—by the name of Humphrey, too—at St. Giles's Church in 1590, and thereafter Couzenses recur on almost every page of the register. Numbers of them were buried during the first half of the eighteenth century, possibly of smallpox; yet numbers managed to persist into late Victorian days. Then the stock dwindled, and though the name is by no means extinct in Stanley Fitzurse, Coffy is the last of the family in Kington Borel.

As a youth he was the bad lad of the village. He was walking out with Louie Keynes in those days, and would bring her every Saturday from the farm where he worked a sheep's henge, pig's trotters, cheek, caul or chitterlings, or when there was a new calf, boycett milk. Louie took the love-offerings readily and made good use of them. The boycett milk became a custard without need of eggs; the chitterlings were soaked, washed, turned inside out, washed again, plaited and boiled; the cheek was converted into brawn, and the liver, minced with bacon and sage and " gibbles " or onions and wrapped in caul, into tasty baked faggots for Sunday supper. But she did not feel that her acceptance of Coffy's presents put her under any obligation to him, and when Will Ody was made foreman at the sawmills she became more interested in him and less in Coffy. Coffy did not intend to lose her so easily. He challenged Will to single combat on the common one night, and won the fight, but not the lady ; and soon afterwards Will and Louie were " called home " in church.

Coffy has remained a bachelor, and " does for " himself —very capably, for there is little he cannot turn his hand to. Mrs. Eeles takes him in his Sunday dinner and does his bit of washing, lest he should neglect it till the dirt was " grinted in," and in return he sees to her garden and makes her wine. This is a convenient arrangement, since Mrs. Eeles can use her copper for laundry only, Coffy his for wine-making only. He is what Mrs. Eeles calls a " dapster " at brewing, and his wines never go " mothery " when the bottom of the cask is reached. He helps on the farms when extra labour is needed, he sweeps chimneys (in thatched cottages they are done three times a year), he knits his own socks, and since he is one of the very few remaining men who can handle a scythe, to him is allotted the task of cutting the churchyard grass every June. He starts before sunrise while the dew is still on the grass and it is " nesh " for cutting, and has finished by sunset of the next day. When the hay is dry he collects it with his big wooden rake. It is an ancient-looking implement, with eleven huge wooden teeth, and the handle consists of a single piece of ash, cleft to within a foot of the end, the two halves being held apart with pegs and clamped one to either end of the rake, where two semi-circular ashen hoops increase its carrying capacity.

Coffy is also a jobbing gardener, and certainly has a green hand ; he maintains that he is the only man in the village who can grow celery. He is a self-made gardener : no wireless tips for him. He is not altogether illiterate : should the occasion demand it, and should he be able to put his hand on the pen (which, through lack of use, is inclined to get mislaid), he can indite a letter of sorts. But he despises book knowledge, and seldom reads even the newspaper. (His mother could not read at all, and always got old Mrs. Archard to read whatever rare letters came her way.) Indeed, as far as gardening is concerned, he despises any opinion but his own, and those who employ him find it best to let him have his own way. The flourishing bushes of sage and rosemary may be proof that the mistress rules the roost, but she cannot rule her garden while Coffy is there. However fond she may be of evening primroses, he will have none of them because they " wrastle " ; she may not like the look of a " wasset-man " or scarecrow among her currant bushes, but he does ; and it is useless for her to think of doing anything so unlucky as to transplant parsley—everyone knows that even when sown it goes to the devil for seven years—or to try to set one kind of potatoes if he has decided on another. It would be little short of blasphemy if they were planted on any other day than Good Friday, or were dug before the haulms were showing signs of flower. Peas and broad beans must be put in when the moon is new, and runner beans are always sown on Coulsham Fair Day, May the sixth.

All country folk think that it is unlucky to see the crescent through glass or to sleep with moonlight streaming on the face ; that if the new moon falls near Christmas the winter will be hard ; that if it lies on its back or holds the old moon in its arms there will be rain ; that plants must grow with the waxing moon and that with the changing of the moon the weather will change. But in the Wiltshireman this veneration for the moon is so great that it lends credence to

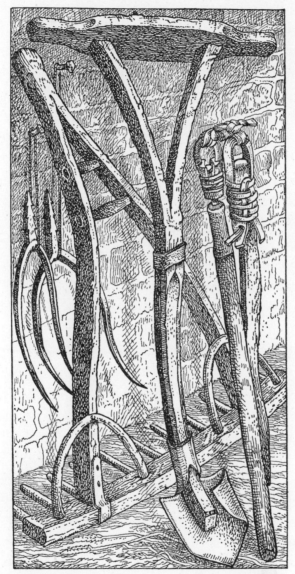

Breast Plough, Threshing Flail (or Drashel),
wooden Hay Rake, and two old Forks.

the legend of the Moonrakers, so fascinated—as they pretended—by its image in the water that they would fain bring it to land.

The countryman's weather-lore is irrational and by no means infallible. There are men in Kington Borel who have worked in the open air all their lives but whose forecasts are seldom reliable. The sense of the true weather prophet, on the other hand, is almost uncanny. Take Henry Bird the woodman. Not only can he say whether the grey sky spells " casalty weather " or merely " blight," or whether wind or sunshine be on the way ; to within an hour or two he knows when clouds will gather or the sun will " bloom out." Yet the reasons he gives for his deductions are often quite unscientific. " Red sky at night, shepherd's delight ; red sky at morning, shepherd's warning," he will quote ; but the novice trying to apply this rule is soon misled unless, like Henry Bird, he can recognise the kind of red that spells settled and the kind that means stormy weather. Sayings in verse are to be trusted with caution, for often reason is sacrificed to rhyme. " Us'll have a main drop of rain," says Henry ; " the leaves be turning their backs and they cows be laying down." (It is fitting that the dwellers in this dairy country should foretell the weather by their cows. If they stand with their tails to the wind there will be rain : if they lie down in the morning it will rain at night, but if they lie down during rain it will not last long !) Sure enough rain comes, even if the cows and the leaves had little to do with it. It was the direction of the wind that Henry had noticed, the halo round the sun, the curdling of the clouds, the clarity of the distant Downs ; but he found the familiar saw the easier explanation.

He would readily share this wisdom if he knew how to do so. But he is less ready to impart the secret whereby he catches rats, for this is a means of livelihood to him. They say that he charms them as Henry Hazell charms warts. Be that as it may, as surely as he visits farm or barn they disappear— only, unlike the warts, they reappear, and he has to make, as a rule, four visits annually, for which he is paid five pounds. " Wants " or moles are a nuisance in the sandy soils, and are trapped by gardeners and farmers. It is no longer thought worth while to pay a man " ten shillings and six pence for his paynes in destroying and killing the Moles or Wants for one whole year." That was in the eighteenth century. Other pests were paid for by the piece—a shilling for five hedge-hogs, or one " gray " or badger, or one fox. The slaughter, justified or unjustified, of animals has caused great changes in the wild life of the neighbourhood during the last few centuries. John Aubrey says that there were " in our grand-fathers' days more foxes than now, and martens (a beast of brown rich furr), the race now extinct." To-day everyone save the gamekeeper leaves hedgehogs alone ; badgers, now few in number, are unmolested except in the hunting season, when they may be ruthlessly dug from their earths and baited by hounds, and every poultry-keeper robbed by foxes shoots for himself when he gets the chance. The local fox-hunt began in 1743 with two foxhounds, Thunder and Giddy. Hitherto there had been harriers and deerhounds only. At the time of its inauguration it was welcomed by farmers as a systematic attempt at keeping down vermin so numerous as to be a menace : they did not foresee that as it developed into an idle pastime for the wealthy it would so far lose sight of its original purpose as actually to defeat it.

The countryman makes no claim to be fond of animals. It may cost him a pang to part with a favourite horse on market day, but he has no use for a cat that cannot kill mice, and the proper place for his dog is out of doors. If it falls sick with some ailment that does not respond to his homely remedies he drowns or shoots it. He sets barbarous gins for rats ; he goes out ferreting ; he beats down rabbits that have been driven by the reaping machine into the last square of standing corn. But if he is ignorant or insensitive he is not usually brutal : if he kills, it is for his livelihood, and in this respect he has outgrown his " betters." This may be due in part to legislation which found it more profitable to curb the poor man's cruel pleasures than those of the rich. " Cock-squailing," or throwing at cocks, for instance, was a favourite sport with the village yokels until it was banned by the Bramelham authorities as " a most Barbarous Practice and not only inconsistent with the Laws both of God and Man, but greatly tending to the training up of Youth in the principles of inhumanity; besides the many accidents which often happen to others from it, and the offence it must naturally give to every good Christian who considers that the Animal World was made for his use and not abuse as such treatment of Cocks most notoriously is." In 1762 a Matthews of Kington Borel was fined at the quarter sessions for cock-squailing on a Shrove Tuesday.

It is as well that Eli Matthews, local preacher at the Methodist Chapel, does not know of this blot on his family escutcheon ; though he would not think it as heinous a crime as " not going to a Place of Worship," which in his view is the root of all evil, at home and abroad. He himself attends three times on a Sunday : at Kington Borel in the

THE WOODMAN

morning and on circuit in the evening, while in the afternoon he trudges to Stanley Fitzurse and conducts a service for a handful of children.

He is now living on the old age pension—it is possible to live on it in this village, where many of the inhabitants have owned their cottages since the days when they could be bought for eighty or ninety pounds—but until his retirement he was a woodman on Priory Farm. Some forty years ago he used to offend his congregation's sense of propriety by preaching in his smock. Yet, being fond of him and unwilling to hurt his feelings, they did not know how to bring to his notice the unseemliness of his costume. At length they thought of a tactful solution, and made some anniversary the excuse for presenting him with a best suit. What was their dismay to see him arrive at chapel on the following Sunday wearing the smock over his suit, lest its smartness should be impaired.

Had the villagers but known it, the smock was infinitely superior to the suit. It was a garment reversible from back to front, and was made of unbleached handspun linen, smocked with white linen thread at the chest, back, wrists and shoulders, and feather-stitched at collar, cuffs and " boxes "—the flat panels on either side of the front and back smocking—with formal designs of trees and leaves symbolical of the woodman's craft. (For the embroidery of a smock varied according to the occupation of the wearer. A shepherd's might be recognised by its curly crooks, a gardener's by its flowers, a dairymaid's by its pattern of hearts.) To be sure, it fitted the figure even less than the ready-made suit ; but, then, it made no pretence of doing so. It was designed to be worn over coats on cold days or instead of them in summer, and so to turn up or down at the collar, while the nature of the stitchery provided a certain amount of elasticity and incidentally gave extra warmth in the most necessary places. Eli's smock must have been one of the last of its kind. Emmy Tucker still makes smocks ; every year she goes the round of the neighbouring farms to do the mending, sometimes staying at one if there are new smocks to be made till the job is done. But Emmy never learnt to do what she calls " frocking," and the smock she makes is devoid of ornament, though it is interesting that in design it has not departed a whit from the original. She will tell you that she has a " pattern " for it, but all she means by that is a few pencilled measurements on a scrap of paper : " Cheast 50, Risbands 12," and so on. The pattern is in her head as she was taught to do it in her girlhood. Nor is it hard to remember, for every piece is square or rectangular. There are two large rectangles for front and back, two for the sleeves, two for shoulder pieces into which the front, back and sleeve smocking must be set, and two narrower ones for the cuffs ; then there must be two squares for the collar and four for gussets—two under the arms and two small ones where the side seams end and front and back fall free as they do on a shirt. It goes without saying that these ample measurements, having no smocking to narrow them, make a somewhat ungainly garment, far inferior to the old smock, yet plainly akin to it, and equally indispensable in the daily life of the farm-hand.

Emmy still does a little dress-making—or more usually dress-altering—for some of her older neighbours ; the younger generation buy ready-mades, or cut out their own scanty frocks from ready-made patterns. Indeed, they would

A Wiltshire Woodman's Smock

not be seen in one of Emmy's clumsy, strongly-stitched garments, that hang from the picture-cords on the walls of her small room, some pinned and awaiting fitting, some tacked, some ready for the final pressing, sombre and voluminous, blotting out the bright colours of " Pilate's Wife's Dream " and " The Broad and the Narrow Way."

The tale of the smock, like most of the village gossip, can be traced to Mrs. Blanchard, the midwife, who at one time " borned " nearly all the Kington babies. When Dr. Bennett lived here she was his right hand ; when the village lost its resident doctor she became still more invaluable, and even now that there is a district nurse she is often in demand for childbirth, the care of young babies, nursing, and laying-out if need be. The ageing villager while yet in possession of his faculties helps her in this solemn ceremony by putting aside in readiness a best night-gown, a chincloth and long white stockings. She feels hurt if she is not sent for when there is a death. On one occasion she thought she had been overlooked. It was when the Mintys lived next door to her. Bert Minty was a very small boy then. One winter evening after he had been " 'ooding " in Herne Wood he came in, as he loved to do, to share his spoils with Mrs. Blanchard. This time the walk had been more exciting than usual. As darkness was falling he and his mother had crossed Pennycroft and were about to enter Herne Wood when they saw a funeral approaching through the trees, and stood aside, frightened, to let it pass. The procession went through the gate and across the field, but beyond that there was no sign of it. Now no-one lived in Herne Wood except the gamekeeper and his wife, and as far as Mrs. Blanchard knew, neither of them was ill. Besides, whoever heard of a funeral taking place at five o'clock ? She thought the story one of Bertie's fictions until it was corroborated by Sarah Minty herself. Mrs. Blanchard felt aggrieved : she had been cheated not only of the laying-out, but apparently of the whole illness. But she was so busy with the Coles' new baby, that did not look as though it intended to live, that the strange happening slipped her memory until the following week, when she was roused at cock-crow by the frantic knocking of the gamekeeper himself. He had just wakened to find his wife lying dead beside him.

Mrs. Blanchard can tell many a tale of the old doctor—how when Thirza Vines was only a slip of a girl, unused as yet to the care of an invalid, he had gone into the kitchen and showed her how to make beef tea and gruel for her sick mother ; how Eddy Eeles' daughter incurred his wrath when she let the old man end his days at the " Spike " ; how when Mrs. Bubb's fourteenth baby was born and she was in a bad way he shook his fist at her husband, crying, " You ought to get six months for this ! " ; how he would tease Nick Hulbert, who was something of an astrologer, when he grumbled that he had Saturn in his stomach ; how he would humour Job Notton's passion for medicine by sending him bottles of coloured water flavoured with peppermint. (It was Job Notton who during his last illness had said when they told him that the Vicar had come to see him, " Oh, I bent as bad as that yet ! ")

All the village mourned when Dr. Bennett left. He has had no successor. It happens that a doctor does live in Kington Borel, but he practises in Bramelham, spending his leisure hours only in the village. A few patients drag themselves to his town surgery, but Kington people nowadays consult a doctor only as a last resort, which is usually when it is too late. "What is the good?" they say. "He only sends you to hospital; Dr. Bennett treated you himself." They have not much opinion of him, neither has he of them. He knows little of their temperaments or their pockets, and thinks it better to tell them as little as possible of what they will certainly not be able to understand. So they spend money they can ill afford on the patent medicines they see advertised. If outside help is needed in spite of—or because of—these, there is Mrs. Blanchard to fall back upon. She is always willing to come, at any hour of the day or night, to administer linseed poultices or hot strong tea and comfort.

Dr. Bennett was more than doctor: he was confidant. Fortunately there is still the Vicar to fulfil this very necessary rôle. Dr. Bennett had right of entry to the houses of all his patients, because if they were abed he must needs let himself in. The Vicar must knock, but he is always admitted, and that cannot be said of every caller. Cottage doors may stand hospitably open all day, but the villager's home is his castle, and he is sensitive as to who shall know as much of him as a glance into his room must reveal. After dark he makes his door fast, and only the most importunate knocking will persuade him to draw the unwilling bolts. The Vicar respects this natural reserve, and often pays his visit when the cottager is at work in the garden. He himself is a keen gardener, and it makes a valuable point of contact with his parishioners. So does his love of children. He is often to be found on the common, teaching the smaller girls how to skip once to two twirls of the rope, or giving the bigger boys a few hints on batting and bowling.

Children's games are much the same here as in any other village, following the same unwritten law of the seasons : tops must be brought out in Lent, hoops in summer, skipping ropes in winter. Children who cannot memorise their seven times table know all the intricacies of hopscotch and of " dibs," a game who knows how old, played with five pebbles or knucklebones. "Hobby onkers," played with horse chestnuts, and "tipcat" are boys' games, and "cut cheese and leapfrog" is not easy to play in a skirt, though some of the more hoydenish girls tuck their dresses into their knickers and join in. "Cut cheese" is the preliminary competition in long-jumping ; the one whose jump falls shortest must be the first to tuck his head in and be leaped over. For some reason it is chiefly boys who play marbles and balls-hole, while girls have their games of make-believe—Mothers, Schools, or Houses, made in ground plan of lines of stones or dust or wet autumn leaves. Girls, too, are fondest of " Steps," in which they command their special friends to advance by " giant strides," while others are kept well in the background with " butterfly steps." Some games are as simple as hopscotch is complicated. " Statues," as everybody knows, is nothing more than a competition in striking attitudes. It is surprising, too, how exciting a pull at a paper " scroll " can be ; though here it is the owner of the scroll who gets the best of the fun ; it is he who makes out on his paper ribbon the list of favourite dinners or Christian names or whatever it may be, rolls it tightly and offers the end to his playmates to unroll. He must use his ingenuity to outwit the greedy scroll-puller who has discovered that all the best things are written at the head of the scroll by making a new one wherein he who pulls modestly will be rewarded.

And in " A pin to see the peep-show "—surely the most innocent of pastimes—the showman is even more delighted than his audience as he proudly displays his mosaic of petals and feathers and other coloured fragments, magical beneath their frame of glass.

Many games, like Touch Wood, Creepmouse, and Wall to Wall, are variations on the themes of " tag " and of " mob " or hide-and-seek, and always there must be some place of sanctuary or " scree." If you should loosen a shoelace or get a stitch in the side when being chased by the ever-increasing chain of taggers in " Sugar-law," for instance, you may even claim " scree " wherever you may happen to be by crossing your fingers—none can touch you until you uncross them and start away again. " Iacker " is always played with Stocks Tree as " home ; " whoever reaches it first, hunter or hunted, must touch the bark and cry " Iacker " as proof of his claim to priority. " Ghost at the Well," too, is staged at Stocks Tree, which happens to be a convenient distance away from the round well-house. For the younger children this lends the game a touch of realism that sometimes proves too vivid when the climax is reached. It is a dramatic little play, with two principal characters, Mother and Ghost, and any number of children, and it follows a fairy-tale pattern :

Children: Please, Mother, may we have some bread and cheese?

Mother : Let me see your hands.

    (The children show them.)

Mother : Go and wash them at the well.

    (The children go to the well. The Ghost, who has

" coopied " down behind it, jumps up and frightens them, and
they come running home.)

Children : Oh, Mother, there's a ghost there !

Mother : Nonsense ; it's only your father's shirt hanging
out to dry. Go again.

    (Again they go and again return with the same story. She
decides to confront the Ghost herself.)

Mother : Oh, well, I suppose I must go with you.

    (She goes to the well, accompanied by her entire brood of
children, and the following dialogue takes place) :

Mother : What are you doing there ?

Ghost : Picking up sticks.

Mother : What do you want the sticks for ?

Ghost : To light my fire.

Mother : What do you want the fire for ?

Ghost : To dry my knives.

Mother : What do you want the knives for ?

Ghost : TO CUT OFF YOUR HEADS !

    (At these words there is a general stampede in the direction
of home, the Ghost pursuing, and the child he catches is the
next Ghost.)

Generations of children have handed on each to the next
the singing games and rhymes, full of nonsense and of
poetry. " Grandmother Gray " is a more domestic version
of " Ghost at the Well." The children cajole their grandmother with :

    " Grandmother, Grandmother Gray,
      May we go out to play ?

We won't go by the riverside
To drive the ducks away."

" Go out and see if it's raining," she says.
They look outside.
" No," they say, " it's not raining."
So she gives her consent. No sooner are they out than
they drive the ducks away, and then it is her turn to chase
them. " Poor Jinny is a-weeping," " I sent a letter to my
love," and the game beginning :

" Wally, Wally, Wallflower growing up so high,
We're old ladies, and we shall have to die."

are all played with hands joined in a ring ; and there is the
tug-of-war game like Oranges and Lemons :

" Draw a bucket of water
For my lady's daughter.
One in a bush,
Two in a bush,
Pray, sweet lady, come under the bush."

Children skip to the rhythm of :

Handy pandy,
Sugardy candy,
French almond rock."

or " Salt, mustard, vinegar, pepper ; " tell their cherry-
stones or their grasses with " Tinker, Tailor ; " count out

whose turn it is with " Ena mena mina mo ; " reckon the
" daps " of their balls to the swing of the long rigmarole
that starts, " One, two, three, alaira ; four, five, six, alaira ;
seven, eight, nine, alaira, tenalaira postboy," warm their
hands when they are "shrammed" with the clapping
rhyme :

> " *My mother said*
> *I never should*
> *Play with the gipsies in the wood " ;*

and quarrel with the retort :

> " *Sticks and stones will break my bones ;*
> *Names will never hurt me.*
> *When I'm dead and in my grave*
> *P'raps you'll think more about me."*

These patterns of pastime and of speech they have woven
for themselves without need of playthings or of suggestion
from the grown-up world ; but on the whole they are
unenterprising. There are children living near Frogwell
who have never been past Allenford Farm, and others at
Bramelham Gate who could not tell you where Sunday Mead
was. If there are some who take more interest in their surroundings it is largely due to the Vicar. In the first place,
they found him useful in telling them where to find the herbs
they collected for pocket money, and the boys discovered
that there was little he did not know about birds. As a young
man he was one of those sportsmen who curiously combine
a love of birds and animals with a love of shooting them ;
he has brought down many a rare duck in his time, and

once a golden oriole. Later the cares of a family and of a parish left him little time for the gun; but he never lost his interest in natural history, and his chief delight is to share it with others, especially with children. By degrees they caught his enthusiasm, and have learned to distinguish hemlock and hogweed from wild celery and angelica, coal-tit from marsh-tit and chiff-chaff from willow-wren.

They have taught him something, too—he has had to learn their names for birds and flowers and insects. A newt is an evet, an ant an emmet, a woodlouse a pig, and a bumblebee a dumbledore. They talk of bannuts, not wal-nuts; bennets, not withered grass; thatch instead of vetch; quitch is their name for the couch grass that runs underground and overground; and they so relish the acid leaves of the sorrel that they call the plant by the pet name of " sadgy." Many of the local words differ little or not at all from Anglo-Saxon. Warm water is " lew-warm "; if you are empty with hunger you feel " leer." Some words, like " teart," the adjective that describes a smarting wound or sour fruit, even preserve the original spelling; many, like " ax " for ask, the original pronunciation. But it is not their pedigree that entitles them to a place in the vocabulary: even old words are discarded if they are out-worn. The fact is that they still supply a need, and therefore they still sound apt and racy. A few are poetical, like " quist " for woodpigeon, and " aftermath " for second crop, but for the most part they are homespun. If one had to invent a word for the weakling of a family, surely it could be none other than " rinnick "—the thin vowels and the diminutive ending spell spindly legs and wizened body. " Scutty " calls to mind the wren's perky tail; " spadgy "

WREN AND PRIMROSES

the rascality of the sparrow. Most vivid are the words for feelings and moods. Chapped hands are " spreathed." A peevish child is " halvish " ; a sulky person is " quampy " ; one slow in the uptake is " dummle." " Comical," on the other hand, no longer conveys the right meaning. It is used to describe an unfriendly, moody attitude, and goes back to the times when persons showing such a temper were believed to be " comet-struck." Some of the words that children use throw light upon child nature. " Berry-moucher " betrays how truants from school often spend their time ; and the bird name " nettle-creeper " shows that boys are less interested in the upturned chin of the warbling whitethroat than in the place where her nest lies hidden.

But it is not in the speech of children that the Wessex language is heard at its richest. Theirs is a slovenly, bastard tongue in comparison with the deliberate utterance of the old people, who give every vowel and every consonant its full value, and even more ; though it is true that their t's and l's, unless they get the start of a word, suffer eclipse, as they do in the daughter language, modern American. It has happened more than once that a Moonraker come to London on holiday has been mistaken for a Yankee—probably because of his " burr," which is the chief as it is the most pleasant feature of his speech. He is quickly recognised as a foreigner of some sort, for Wiltshire is the antithesis of Cockney. The Londoner tends to turn dipthongs into pure vowels, the Wiltshireman to make polysyllables of monosyllables. " Night " and " down," which are " naht " and " dahn " within the sound of Bow Bells, are " noi-eet " and " dow-wun " at Kington Borel Market Cross.

173

This " drawning speech, something heavy and melancholy," may be heard on many lips in Kington Borel—from Tom Coates reciting the Lord's Prayer in church, from Caleb Drewett singing to his cows as he milks them, from Will Hancock, who, thinking his two small grandchildren too young to join in the big bonfire festivities, says as he relentlessly stamps out the last red glow of the small pyre he has built for them in the back garden, " Thur. Thee'st 'ad thee bonvier and thee'st 'ad thee vierwurks, and now thee canst go to bed." And it may be heard at its most fluent from Joe Garlick, who has an excellent memory which time has not dimmed but has the rather embroidered. He remembers when the stocks stood under Stocks Tree ; as a small boy he saw one John Langley doing penance there for drunkenness. He requires but little persuasion to tell his famous tale of the " reshit " that haunted the farm where he used to work. "I can moind," says he, "when I wur up Whoam Varm, us dursn't go noigh thic stavel barn noights for the reshit as did wallop and bump on thic drashing vloor. Ah, and 'twurn't on'y in the barn, noither: a did get in thic byre and tie they hosses' manes all in gurt knots-loike, so as us wur fair put to it ta onloosen of 'em. Us did make the lock fast noights, but thic reshit must a crope drough the keyhole or leastways down in under the door, and come marnin' they was all a-twisted up zame as avore. Varmer wur in a vair caddle. Fust when us telled un what we seen, a thowt us'd 'ad a drop too much tiddly. " Thee ca'sn't zee so well as thee cou'st, ca'st ? " a says, nasty-loike. Then when a zeed for hissen a kep' a-broibin' o' we and says as us done it; then a did twit us as us was aveard to go past the barken arter dark. Wull, it come zo's I couldn't aboide it no longer, and one noight I says as I 'ud go up thic varm fur to watch fur they ghostieses. I 'adn't but just come out the drung atween Laweses's housen and ourn when I sees Will Clapp. " Wur bist thee gwine, you ? " a says. I tells un and a says, " Thee best boide wur thee bist, Joe." Howsumdever, a zees as I wur set on't and a comes along of 'I. Us wurn't no more'n a lug from thic barn when us heared zummat. " 'E be the reshit ! " I says. " Do zound loike a main vew on 'em," a says. " Awpen thic thur geat and get atop of thic thur mixen, Joe," a says, " and peek in at un." I never heared sich a rumpus as come then : 'twur loike as if zomebody wur drashing with a 'nation gurt drashel. Me swallow wur as dry as a gix, and Will 'e wur all of a shiver, but anyways a crope up the mixen and I did climb up atop of 'e. . . .

But I never seed nowt.

No, and nobody never zeed nowt, noither. Volks as never heared un did say as thiccun wurn't no reshit and thur wurn't narn. Zum di zay as 'twur old Nick hissen. I 'ouldn't loike fur to zay as 'twur . . . And then, I 'ouldn't loike fur to zay as 'twurn't."

Joe Garlick can tell many a tale of the old Squire, too. In those days none of the womenfolk would dream of passing Squire or his wife without dropping a curtsey. If there was a child in the village in need of a new pair of boots Squire must be notified of the fact, and Timothy Hancock, who was bailiff at the time, would be sent to investigate the claim. On his recommendation Squire would write out an order on a certain Bramelham bootmaker—and the cost of the boots was deducted from the father's wages. Once George Notton was coming home from Goosey Acre with a good supper of mushrooms tied up in his neckerchief

when whom should he meet but Squire, whose eagle eyes
spotted the bundle. " What have you got there ? " he cried.
Old Notton was forced to yield up the spoils, and it was
Squire who enjoyed a mushroom supper that night. However, it does not require a memory as long as Joe Garlick's
to recall this abject fear of Authority. Mrs. Comely remembers, as clearly as though it were yesterday, a day in her own
childhood when she came running home in tears because her
small brother had inadvertently said " Good-morning " instead of " Good-afternoon " to the Vicar. He would think
it had been done on purpose. He would tell Squire. They
would all be turned out of their house. In spite of this,
Mrs. Comely has grown up with dangerously democratic
ideas : if Miss Tarrant comes into the shop after Sarah
Minty she serves her after Sarah, and not, as her mother
would have done, before.

She has, notwithstanding, much sympathy with Mrs.
Archard's generation, and says the old lady would turn in her
grave could she but see some of the goings-on of to-day—
young Freda Romaine celebrating her freedom from school
on her fourteenth birthday by a permanent wave, Mrs. Clapp
rushing into the shop at half-past nine on a Saturday night
for quarter-pounds of sugar and cocoa, a tin of salmon,
" boughten " cake and jam, and two penn'orth of sweets for
the children, all to be " put down on the account." Mrs.
Comely and her brothers and sisters had no sweets in their
childhood ; if they asked for them their mother doled them
out handfuls of raisins and currants. There was more work
to be done too—walking to Bramelham on shopping errands,
taking back the basket of washing to some big house (Mrs.
Archard was paid sixpence for doing a week's wash), or

" leasing " in the fields after harvest. They hated this job—
the stubble was so prickly ; but the chickens had to be fed.
Extravagance was, in fact, the deadliest of the seven sins.
When Dolly Archard one fine morning, forgetting her fruit
tart in the oven, went off to town in her Sunday best—for
in spite of her careful upbringing she grew up to be somewhat gay—she returned to find its blackened remains set
accusingly on the kitchen table, and by them a piece of paper
on which was written in her father's handwriting : " May
you never live to want it." He was a grim old man : on the
eve of Dolly's marriage to that good-for-nothing, Alf
Rawlings, he sent as his wedding gift a mirror and a rope,
that she might look in the one to see what a fool she was,
and with the other hang herself.

The gloom of country life is seldom exaggerated in fiction. These are not light-hearted people, nor were they when
Aubrey knew them : " North Wiltshire is very worm-
woodish. The men and women be strong and something
warm and well-coloured, but slow and dull, heavy of spirit.
Hereabout is but little tillage or hard labour ; they only milk
the cows and make cheese ; they feed chiefly on milk meates,
which cooles their braines too much and hurts their inven-
tions. It is a woodsere country, abounding much with sowre
and austere plants, as sorrel etc., which makes their humours
melancholy and fixes their spirits."
The villager's is a fatalistic philosophy. Does a fruit tree
blossom out of season ? " There'll be another on us to
go." What is to be is to be. Of course there is such a thing
as tempting Providence. It does not do, for example, to set
your signature to paper. The form and the petition are to

be eschewed, for once name and address are there in black and white " They," who are almost as omnipotent as Squire himself, will know where you live and how many children you have ; and it would be asking for trouble to set more or less than thirteen eggs under a broody hen. But if you set thirteen, and still they do not hatch, then that " was to be."

It is not surprising that most of the village electorate, if they vote at all, vote Conservative. For one thing, many of them are in the employ of the " big houses." Moreover, it is not safe to interfere with the status quo, for it follows as a natural corollary of " What is to be is to be " that " What has been will be," or as old Mrs. Couzens used to put it, " I brought trouble into the wordle when I come into the wordle, and I've 'ad trouble ever since."

There is something very touching in this resignation of the will to the powers that be, both spiritual and temporal. At the worst it is apathy : at the best it is stoical courage. And if they are content to let politicians do their worst with home and foreign affairs, they are also content with their own work, that leaves them little time for question. They are too busy living to want to " see life."

" What always has been always will be." It is natural that this should be the village creed ; there are times when one could even wish it were true, and that the daily round might be repeated unto eternity—birdsong in the small hours, sunrise over the combe, the farmer calling to his two cart-horses and slipping halters over their willing necks, a woman dipping her crook into the well and hanging out her washing, ducks on the pond and children on the common, the rumble of a farm cart, the clink of the smithy, the sound of the church bells at evening when cottagers tend their gardens and the old men sit on the steps of the Market Cross ; then the last light going out under the eaves as the village falls asleep.

THE END

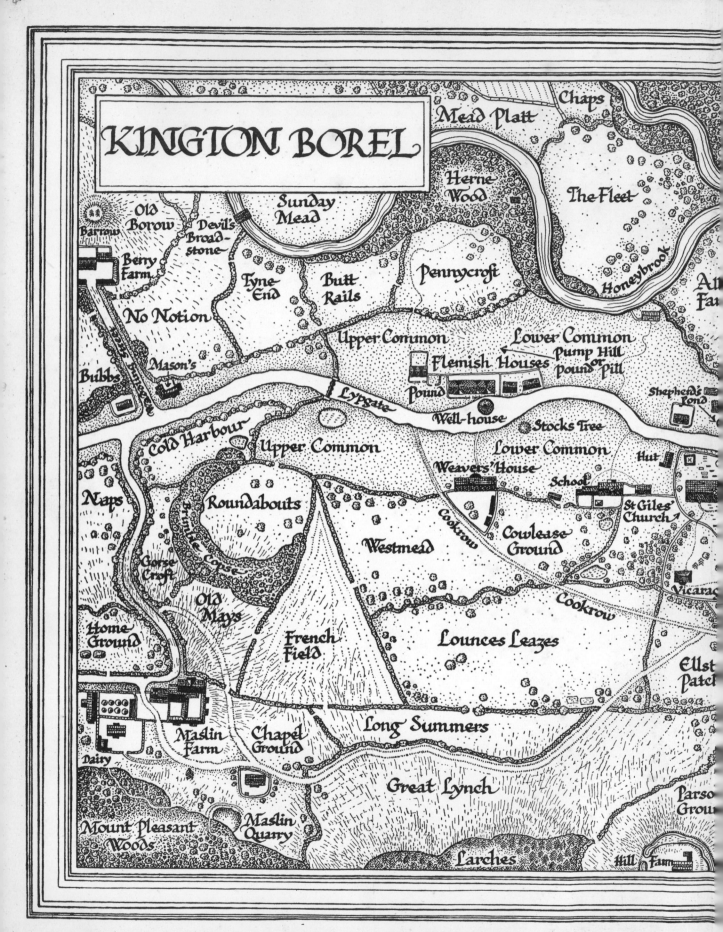